I pray this book take your life to new levels because Broken should never feel Right

— Michael J.

whenbroken2@gmail.com

MILDRED "MICKEY" GIVENS

When

Broken

Feels

Right

Dedication

I would like to dedicate my first book, "When broken feels right" to my granddaughter, Ciniyah. Well, Well, Well.

Contents

Acknowledgments

First, I want to thank and acknowledge God for his insight and courage throughout the entire writing process. I simply could not have done it without him. Secondly, I must recognize some individuals who were instrumental in helping me complete the book. No matter how small or great your contribution may have been, I want to thank you. You might have read my manuscript, and offered feedback. You might have intently listened as I read parts of my book to you, then offered your constructive criticism. You may have offered suggestions, assistance or referred or recommended someone who could assist in the writing process. You simply may have encouraged me by saying, "I'm proud of you, you can do this, I believe in you, or how is the book going?" Your interest, support and words of encouragement made the writing process invigorating, exciting and worthwhile. So, with much heartfelt gratitude, I would like to acknowledge and thank the following individuals; Terrence Givens, Dr. Natalie Young, Delana Givens, Ciniyah Young, Cydnee Young, Iris Young, Pam Powell, Eddie Jackson, Denzel Henderson, Helen Crawley-Austin, HK Wilson, River Jones, my proofreaders, Editor Unique Ph.D., ▓▓▓▓▓▓▓▓▓▓▓▓▓ ▓▓▓▓▓ Last but not least, I must thank my biggest cheerleaders, my parents, the late Milton and Callie Britton. They were the first to encourage and support my many endeavors. With much love and appreciation, I truly thank you all.

Chapter 1
Discovery

Awakening

It was three in the morning and I laid flat on my back in my cold dark bedroom. As I reached out into the dark in search of my husband, I only found even colder sheets on his side of the bed. His side of the bed was once again empty, void of his presence. At that moment, I pulled the comforter from his side of the bed and pulled it over my shoulders in an attempt to warm myself and get a whiff of his stale cologne, which often lingered on his side of the bed. As I pulled the comforter and the scent of his stale cologne closer to me, I thought to myself, "He had to work over again; he is such a hard worker, a great provider, a wonderful husband, a loving father, I love him so much." And with those thoughts, I started to drift back to sleep, but as I drifted into what was now an uneasy rest, I heard a small soft voice from somewhere deep within me respond with Lies! Lies! All lies! Why do you continue to lie to yourself? I know why I had lied, and I know why I had continued to lie to myself for years. I lied because it felt right, it felt easy. Now I think that's the real reason. That it was easy. It had become easy to pretend that I still loved this man as much as I did years ago. It was easy to pretend an orgasm when we had sex and it had become easier to ignore all the obvious signs of his infidelity. It was easy to ignore the fact that my marriage was broken and yet it felt right.

How can brokenness feel right? How do you become comfortable in brokenness? Let me explain, elaborate, and expound on the subject matter. I believe the majority of the time brokenness does not feel right. Normally when something is broken, for example, a broken heart or a broken spirit, we often feel hurt, sad, disappointed, depressed, and even ill. Broken is often described as something separated into two or more pieces through the process of being hit, cut, torn, or damaged by similar forces. Other commonly known definitions of brokenness are; not working properly, sorrowful, disconnected, made weak, and crushed. The term brokenness has several negative connotations. That being so, then let me pose the question; how can broken feel right? I asked that exact same question when debating on a title for this book. "_When broken feels right_". I also asked myself exactly what does that mean? And this is what I came up with. It's an idea, a concept, it's a conscious or unconscious act of accepting mistreatment, poverty, sickness, injustice, moreover falsehood and other debilitating circumstances and or accepting debilitating behaviors, which lead to and can cause individuals over a period of time to become comfortable within defeat, weakness, lack, and similar deprivations. In other words, when you spend a given amount of time in negative situations or with negative individuals you become more prone to adapt, conform to, and even defend one's brokenness.

Acceptance

I must admit that was not the first time I heard that small soft voice. I heard it many times throughout the 22 years of my marriage. When I heard the voice, I would often shift my attention or I kept myself busy with household chores or errands in an attempt to ignore and drown out the voice. For several years I attempted to ignore the voice by responding with positive affirmations. For example, if the voice told me "It's late, and he's out again in the arms of another woman." I would then respond, "No he is not, he is working overtime and he has gotten too busy to call me." Oftentimes the voice would tell me, "Look, he is whispering on the phone again, he is talking to one of his mistresses." I would then respond, "No he is not, my husband loves me and he is faithful to our marriage." I rejected, argued, and debated with that small soft voice for many years until one day the voice said, "He is scratching again, I bet you he has a sexually transmitted disease." The voice continued, "And do you remember the time when you found condoms in his suitcase when he returned from out of town and the time you found condoms in the garage, hidden in his toolbox?" Lastly the voice said, "And do you remember the time you found that empty condom box in his bottom drawer, pushed toward the back and buried under his old T-shirts?" This time there was no quick retort, no arguing, no debate, nor even a verbal affirmation. I responded with silence, followed by reflections, contemplation, and then acceptance. I could no longer ignore or reject common sense. I not only accepted the wisdom of that small inner voice but I also accepted the fact that I was at a point and a place in my life that I did not want to be.

Reality

After awakening to what seemed like a deep sleep, I came to realize that I had drifted far from my life dreams, goals, and aspirations. I had planned to be happily married. Eventually, I would be an empty nester, then early retirement, traveling and vacationing with a loving, caring, and supportive husband. I had also planned to invest more time with my children, grandchildren, friends, family, hobbies, and business adventures. But instead, I found myself divorced, devastated, and in distress. How did I get here? How did I become so complacent, content, and conforming within a broken marriage? Let me tell you how; now picture, and imagine this. It is similar to sitting in a bright, sunny, well-lit room. As the sun begins to set, shades of gray slowly fill the room, which creates shadows across the walls. As the sun continues to set, the shades of gray thicken and the shadows on the wall darken. Your eyes gradually adjust to the dim light now within the room. Just before the sun completely sets, your pupils dilate and gradually adjust to the dark hues and shades of gray that now blanket the entire room. Now sitting in a dark room, you are amazed that you can still make out shapes and objects within the room. And because you have sat there so long, you are now comfortable within the darkness. I realized I had become that person sitting comfortably in the dark. I had also reached a place in my life where I no longer even miss the warm beautiful rays of the sun.

In retrospect, that scenario was similar to my broken marriage. As the sun of respect, faithfulness, and trust slowly set, thick dark shadows of betrayal, lies, and neglect gradually blanketed my marriage. And I found myself sitting within a cold, dark relationship. Because I had sat there so long, I became more comfortable. I had also reached a place where I no longer looked for the warm beautiful rays of affection, compassion, respect or even love. After facing the reality that my marriage was broken and yet it felt right, I contemplated on other possible areas in my life that may be broken. I wondered had my eyes slowly adjusted to dim, heavy shades and hues of gray that possibly engulfed other rooms of my life? What about the financial, spiritual, physical, or maybe the mental areas of my life? Had I also unconsciously become comfortable sitting in darkness within these areas as well? Have you?

Reflection

Is it possible to settle, to become comfortable with less, lack, and other limitations and not know it? Yes, it is possible, because I did, and I did it for years. I had not only accepted abuse but I had also become comfortable with mistreatment, disrespect and other degenerative behaviors and circumstances which prevented me from experiencing and living a more prosperous and abundant life. Is it possible that you're not wealthier, healthier, wiser, or experiencing more positive relationships because you have settled for abundant debt, poverty, sickness, weakness, ignorance, lies, and abusive and toxic relationships? Even worse, have you settled for less and don't even know it? Within the following chapters, I share with you how I was able to identify, define and mend some broken areas within my life. I do so by honestly sharing some of my personal life experiences and the life experiences of others. My hope is that by doing so, it creates an opportunity and a desire to take an inventory of the areas of your life. And if need be, confront and correct the broken areas in your life because broken should never feel right.

Chapter 2
Broken
Relationships

Introduction

Broken relationships are any partnerships, associations, or connections to individuals that prevent you from expressing your true, honest, or creative self. You might develop feelings of less than or be made to feel inadequate and unappreciative. Verbal, mental, and physical abuse can often be found within broken relationships. Any relationship has the potential to break, for example; spouses, siblings, co-workers, friends, neighbors, lovers and the list is endless. Within this chapter, I would like to share with you some broken aspects of my once marriage.

A Broken Marriage

I was married for 22 years and prior to that, I had invested almost 9 years in an on-again/off-again relationship with the same man. I had invested a little over 30 years into that relationship. To be honest I had known for many years that my marriage was broken. It was actually broken from the start. Over the years, I came to realize that my marriage was broken partly because it stemmed from two badly broken individuals. My once spouse and I both saw the cracks and dents within each other, but we ignored them. Maybe we thought the cracks would magically fix themselves with the passing of time. For many years I thought he would change, and for many years I thought I could help him change. At the start of the marriage, I recall thinking to myself "I can fix him; he will change after we get married." Now be honest; have you ever told yourself that you could fix or change your spouse? I did, on numerous occasions, but the least to say, it didn't work.

Side Streets

I recall one night I spotted my husband in traffic. He was about three cars ahead of me. I assumed he was on his way home, so I attempted to pull up behind him. Once he reached the intersection, he unexpectedly made a right turn onto a wide street and parked. He was only about a mile or so from our residence. Unbeknown to him, I pulled up and parked directly behind him. Immediately a woman emerges from one of the nearby houses, approaches his car, and gets in. At that point for some reason, I put my high beams on for some reason. Don't ask me why, it was my first reaction to the situation. Then I sat there for about 30 seconds which seemed like forever. Then I pulled off and drove directly home. In less than 10 minutes, he arrived at the house extremely angry, frustrated, and agitated. Instead of apologizing and explaining who this lady was, he immediately started yelling and ranting. He was very accusatory and belligerent. He continued to stress the fact that he was very displeased at the fact that I shined my car's high beams into the back window of his car. He offered no apology nor explanation, but he did offer advice; he advised me never to do that again. He also questioned me as to why I was in that location, on that street at that particular time of the night. In a matter of minutes, he was able to dominate the conversation and switch roles. I was now in the hot seat, on the witness stand, to sort of speak. He accused me of following him and spying on him. He avoided and ignored the obvious subject, which was the fact that he had just picked up a lady who only lived roughly a few miles away; he didn't even attempt to lie. Normally when he lies, he would constantly repeat himself. So, it was evident that he didn't want to start telling lies, and I definitely didn't want to hear them.

Hidden Treasures

In addition to the many lies he told, I also thought about the many times I caught him up late at night whispering on the phone. I also thought about the many times he came home around 10 or 11 PM, considering that he got off work at three. I also thought about the fact that we seldom went out on the weekends. I thought about the fact that he never left his cell phone laying around, he always hid it. I also thought about the fact that he hid his car keys and the fact that he kept his car locked even when it was parked in the garage. It was an attempt to prevent me from having access to his car. But every now and then he would forget to lock his car. Within his car he kept under lock and key what I called his hidden treasures. I often found the following items: his flight itinerary, that outlined his rendezvous to meet his mistress on any given weekend, a bottle of his special cologne, a CD mix of old-school love ballads, condoms, flyers, pluggers, and other glossy invitations to parties and events. In his armrest I would find telephone numbers scribbled on pieces of paper or on bar napkins revealing a name and a telephone number. There was also cash; on the average maybe $150, mostly in the denomination of twenty- dollar bills. On the back seat I would often locate a Marshall's bag which often contained a couple of new t-shirts and or underwear, along with a new shirt or two with the sales tag still attached which often revealed a 30% to 50% discount. Sometimes his cell phone would be found among the many treasures. I thought about all his treasures, his unfaithfulness, I also thought about the verbal, and physical abuse, but strangely, I didn't think about leaving him.

A Faded Rose

We were in our twentieth plus years of marriage, and I still thought or had hopes that we could save what little marriage we had left. Midway through the marriage, I did leave on three occasions. I also returned on three occasions. We reconciled, went to counseling, and implemented new suggestions, techniques, behaviors, and trigger words that were supposed to help us recognize trouble areas within the marriage. The goal was to become closer, more respectful, and gain more understanding of each other's feelings and needs. We were both willing to try. I recall on occasions; maybe on Valentine's Day, he would buy me flowers. But I couldn't help to think and wonder who else he bought flowers for on Valentine's Day. As usual, I smiled, thanked him, and told him how beautiful the flowers were. I knew later that day or maybe later in the week someone else would be thanking and showing him their appreciation and affection for some roses as well. My ex-husband would sometimes buy me roses after he was caught in a lie, or an adulterous affair. For a while, I had grown to dislike roses because they only reminded me of my husband's infidelity and unfaithfulness. I recall on one occasion; he bought me twelve long-stem roses; although they were very beautiful, they were only a reminder of his infidelity. It was so ironic, as I thought about it. I had placed his infidelity which was represented as twelve beautiful red long stem roses into a vase, surrounded by fresh white baby breath with a beautiful bright red silk ribbon, perfectly tied into a beautiful bow. Every 3-4 days I would remove the infidelity from the vase, add flower food to the water and then place the flowers back into the vase. This was all done in an attempt to keep the infidelity bright and colorful and on display for at least two weeks. The flowers were a daily reminder of his unfaithfulness. It was as if his infidelity was displayed right in the middle of my dining room or kitchen table until it withered, dried up and its petals fell onto the table. It's ironic how as the roses withered and faded, so did his commitment to be true and faithful.

Why Stay?

You might ask why I stayed so long? Considering everything I endured. The physical, verbal abuse, blatant disrespect, lies, and infidelity. For a span of 22-plus years. Initially, I honestly thought I could help change him. Then I thought marital counseling would help him change and save our marriage. But to no avail, he stayed the same. Over the years I was the one that changed. I became accepting, conforming, and comfortable within a toxic relationship. I truly believe another reason why I stayed is because of my religious beliefs and upbringing as it related to divorce. I remember growing up; I was always encouraged to get married, support my husband, and work through marital disagreements. I did exactly that; I made great attempts to work through every marital problem, even domestic abuse, which was also both physically and mentally stressful and strenuous. I often ask myself why did I stay? Could it have been that I loved him so much and was hoping that he would change, or could it have been that I had nowhere else to go, or could it have been that I needed help financially? Not quite sure why I stayed, but I did realize that I stayed way too long.

Domestic Violence

Years ago, a friend of mine dated an abusive man for several years. She shared with me several horror stories resulting from this abusive relationship. I asked her why she stayed. She would often explain that he was really a nice guy when he wasn't under the influence of drugs and or alcohol. It was the days that he was nice that she tried to focus on. But there were days when the abuse was unbearable and she would literally flee her home in the middle of the night. She often took refuge at a neighbor's house or a nearby relative's home until he was able to calm down and or sleep off his drunken stupor or detox from one of his quick drug fixes. She would call all- hours of the night, in distress, flabbergasted, and sometimes fearing for her life. I remember the first night she called asking for money in an attempt to move, to escape the abuse. I was so excited because I thought to myself that she had finally built enough strength, and courage to leave this toxic, demoralizing relationship. With the financial support she received from myself and others, she was able to move in less than a week. I was overjoyed that this young lady had decided to seek a better life, one free of abuse and tyranny. But my excitement was short-lived; in less than two weeks, she reunited and moved back in with her abusive partner. I was taken aback, surprised and in dismay.

I noticed a pattern within the months that followed. She would move out again and move back in again. It was actually very painful and stressful to watch her live such a destructive lifestyle. I just couldn't grasp or understand why she had chosen to live in such a demoralizing relationship. So, I began to seeking answers, answers that would give me a better understanding of her situation. I was referred to a counselor, one who specialized in domestic violence. He shared with me some very helpful facts and information. The counselor informed me that domestic violence does occur in many forms, for example sexual, physical, emotional, and the threat of abuse by an intimate partner. Although men are sometimes abused, domestic violence is often directed toward women. Over the years domestic violence has increased. On average, in the United States, it has been estimated that over ten million individuals are abused every year. The counselor also stressed that support is extremely important. He encouraged me to support the young lady and not to be critical or judgmental. He also stressed the importance of allowing her to be free to make her own decision, to either stay or leave the abusive relationship. The choice is hers. Although it may be difficult to observe a friend and or a loved one suffer at the hands of an abusive partner, it's still imperative to be respectful of their decision. The young lady remained in that abusive relationship for over seven years. Now looking back, I can recall thinking to myself I would never allow anyone to mistreat me the way she was mistreated. Mind you; this took place years before I was married. Back then, I could not have imagined living in an abusive relationship let alone an abusive marriage. Nevertheless, years later, there I was, I found myself married and living in a similar situation.

Opening Doors.

After my divorce, I was able to identify and target several broken areas of my life. I didn't realize how comfortable I had become with rejection and the lack of common courtesy. When I first met my ex - husband he used to open doors for me, but it was very short-lived. A few years after my divorce, I ran into an old friend at an event. Because I had taken an Uber, he offered to drop me off at a nearby restaurant where I was meeting some friends. When the event ended, we walked out of the building and walked in the direction of his car which was parked near the back of the parking lot. As we approached his car, I reached for the door handle of the car and at that moment he quickly positioned himself between me and his car door. While unlocking the car, he stated "Oh no, let me get the door for you." He opened the door and politely waited as I got in, then he gently and securely shut the door. Once he was in the car, he waited for me to put my seatbelt on and even asked if I was comfortable before he pulled off. When we arrived, he parked directly in front of the restaurant. He then got out of the car, walked around to my door, opened it, extended his hand and gently assisted me out of the car. Although it was a simple act of courtesy, I felt amazing, and so special. I had not been treated like that in a very long time, it felt really good.

His polite mannerism actually took me aback. At that moment, I realized I had missed those qualities in a man. For most of my marriage, my ex-husband was not very courteous. During and after my marriage I had become comfortable opening doors and pulling out chairs for myself. One Sunday morning, I observed a couple leaving the church. The family consisted of the husband, his wife, and their two high school-age daughters. The husband pulled up in front of the main doors of the church, where his wife and two daughters were waiting. He stepped out of the car, and he first opened the door for his wife. He then proceeded to open the door for his daughter who sat directly behind his wife. He quickly maneuvered to the opposite side of the car, and opened the back door for his other daughter, who sat directly behind the driver's seat. I stood there in the middle of the parking lot and observed his behavior. Seeing a father exhibit such loving gestures in front of his family was just amazing to me. His behavior spoke volumes about his character. It was obvious that his wife and daughters were accustomed to being treated as such. Within my past marriage, I had become accustomed to being treated quite the opposite.

You Can't Have Your Cake And Eat It Too

I knew of a young lady; let's just call her Barbie. She lived with a man for roughly five years and during that time she gave birth to two of his children. Barbie was very happy and very much in love. The man was eight years her senior. He lived in a nice house, he owned two cars and a truck, he had a good job, and he also had a wife. Barbie never liked to think of the fact that the man she was in love with was also married. For five years he had promised her they would get married as soon as he filed for divorce. Some days she believed him, other days she believed her mother who often told her that he would never marry her. "He can't have his cake and eat it too." Her mother would often repeat this phrase on a regular basis. It's a very old phrase that basically describes an individual who wants two things that are seemingly impossible to possess at the same time. Usually, they want something that is difficult or impossible to obtain. For example, this man appeared to want to remain married to his wife, and raise a second family with his mistress. Sadly, Barbie remained within that broken relationship for several years.

Reflection

Can you relate to any of the above experiences? Have you experienced the exact, or similar situation in any of your relationships? Are there individuals in your life who are continuously disrespectful, belligerent, rude, and or possibly abusive? Why would anyone remain in such a deplorable relationship? There are hundreds of reasons as to why someone would stay, but I personally stayed because I thought things would change. Well, things did change; things briefly changed for the better, then quickly went back to bad, then to worse, and eventually, I found myself at the lowest point in my life. Even at that low point in my life, I was still hopeful and hoping that everything would just work itself out. But things didn't get better, things didn't fix themselves. Things became broken, and I became comfortable with the brokenness. I cannot pinpoint when it happened, it was so subtle. Over time his negative behavior became so familiar. Over time I have come to discover that familiarity breeds contentment and contentment often creates complacency and comfortability.

Chapter 3
Broken
Thoughts

Introduction

Many factors contributed to the breakdown and dismantlement of my marriage. Some most commonly known factors were money, communication, oh and of course his infidelity. There was also one other factor that I initially had not considered. This one factor was very pertinent, very influential and it greatly contributed to the breakdown of the marriage; that factor was broken thoughts. It was the way in which my ex-husband discerned, and viewed people, and in general, the world in which we lived. Broken thoughts are any mental images that continuously create and or encourage tension, stress, fear, hatred, and the likes thereof. Broken thoughts often lead to broken feelings which are often expressed in broken words, which can be expressed in broken behavior. Ultimately broken behavior can create a broken environment, which in my case led to an unhappy home, which led to a divorce. Whether negative or positive, your thoughts have the ability to touch and affect every aspect of your life. The following are a few topics and subjects in which I discovered broken thoughts. I encourage you to take a close look and consider your own train of thought as you decipher the following topics.

Judgmental

I was out shopping one day, and while standing in the checkout aisle, preparing to purchase my groceries, I noticed a young lady approaching. She was accompanied by a young man who appeared to be her boyfriend or possibly her husband. They both revealed many bright-colored tattoos on their arms, legs, chest, and their necks. They both had several body and ear piercings. The young lady had her nose and navel pierced. She wore a very form-fitting outfit, which left very little to the imagination. She had straight blonde hair with red streaks throughout, which hung a little past her shoulders. The young man also had blond, and fiery red hair; which was ear length on one side, and completely shaved off on the opposite side of his head. I'm ashamed to admit it, but my first mental response was very judgmental. Once I saw them, I immediately started to negatively judge their character and personality based on their tattoos, hair styles, body piercings, and their attire.

As I stood in the checkout line, I noticed that they appeared to be comparing the length of the lines. They were searching for the shortest line, which happened to be the one I was in. As they maneuvered their grocery cart directly behind me, their food cart hit the back of my leg. I immediately heard a soft voice say, "I am so sorry. Are you ok?" They were surprisingly both very apologetic and friendly. I was taken aback. Their outward appearances gave no indication of their inwardly warm and pleasant personalities. After she apologized a couple of times, the young lady, her boyfriend and I briefly engaged in pleasantries. We briefly talked about the crowded store, high food prices, and the weather. All the while, I'm thinking this is a very pleasant conversation and that they are surprisingly kind and courteous. Do you often have preconceived judgmental thoughts? How often have you been quick to judge someone based on their appearance?

Disabled Not ~~Deaf~~ Deaf

We often become comfortable with prematurely judging the population of non-ambulatory individuals. Our society is often very judgmental about our population of individuals who are wheelchair-bound, and/or those individuals who use a cane or walker to assist them with their mobility. For many years I worked with disabled children and adults, both physically and mentally impaired. I noticed throughout the years that they often shared similar struggles and life stories. Many of the students shared a common challenge with being confined to a wheelchair. Besides the obvious; curbs, stairs, and narrow doorways, they also faced challenges dealing with individuals' preconceived notions in regards to their disabilities.

Several of the students shared with me that people tend to raise their voices when they meet them for the first time. One student candidly shared with me that on several occasions he wanted to respond in a loud voice, "I'm disabled, not deaf." It still escapes me today as to why some individuals believe or assume someone in a wheelchair is hard of hearing.

So often Individuals confined to a wheelchair are often misjudged and or mislabeled as mentally retarded, which is an offensive and outdated term. Because of negative connotations the term "mentally retarded" has been changed to intellectual disability, roughly since 2013. Many of our disabled population are often looked upon with ▄▄▄▄ glances of bewilderment and or pity. One student explained to me how he was able to overcome ▄▄▄▄, the whispers, and sometimes blatant finger-pointing. He would often say hello and start a conversation with a stranger or a passerby. Once engaged in a conversation the stranger will often appear to become more relaxed and even comfortable enough to ask about his disability. They will often time, look timidly at first ask, then "What happened? How did you end up in a wheelchair?" Which in turn gave him an opportunity to educate and enlighten yet another confused and misinformed individual. The young man went on to explain that his goal was to educate and encourage misguided and misinformed men and women to learn about disabled individuals. By doing so, he believes this is his small way of motivating people one conversation at a time. He hopes to help fight against society's broken thoughts, stereotypes, and preconceived notions about physical disabilities.

Road Trip

I know a young lady who I will refer to as Dot. She has lived on the west side of Chicago for most of her life. Growing up was very difficult. Both of her parents struggled with substance abuse. For most of her childhood, she was raised by her single mother. During her young school years, she fought and struggled against the temptation to get involved with gangs, drugs, alcohol, and other temptations that plague many of our impoverished inner-city youth. As a young adult, she fought to secure and maintain steady employment. Most of her time and the majority of her years were invested in an environment and in people who both appeared to be struggling. For the majority of her life, she had been fighting to survive. I knew she wasn't presented with many opportunities to travel. For many years she was unable to travel out of state, if only for a quick getaway to relax or to enjoy a simple vacation. One summer I decided to ask her to join my family and I on a road trip, which she was delighted to go. The destination was Nashville Tennessee, to visit one of my cousins, who had recently moved into her new home.

It was a beautifully decorated spacious five-bedroom, with four bathrooms, walk-in closets, vaulted ceilings, and several other amenities. After the initial excitement, hugs and kisses, a tour of the house, and the release of fatigue and minor stress which one often experiences when driving for several hours in a confined vehicle, I noticed the young lady appeared to be in deep thought. I approached her and asked her to share her thoughts with me. Dot explained that she had never imagined being in such a beautiful and spacious home. Further into the conversation, she also admitted that she could not imagine living in such a home. At that time in her life, she was sharing a small rented apartment with some of her family members. Many of her friends and other family members lived a similar lifestyle. This was the lifestyle she was exposed to on a regular basis. It was this same continuous exposure that created her comfort zones. She had become comfortable, settled, and accepted her small cramped living arrangements as normal. She expressed that she had never known anyone who not only lived in such a house but who could afford such a house. The owner of the house attempted to persuade Dot that with persistence, perseverance, and determination she could also purchase a home similar to or even larger than his. Dot quickly dispelled and disagreed with the homeowner. She abruptly shouted out and with conviction, "absolutely not, there is no way I could ever live in a big, nice house like this!" She did not know that the owner had also grown up within similar circumstances, and an almost identical environment as hers. Dot was so adamant that she would never be able to experience the finer things in life. Her beliefs were greatly influenced by her environment which in turn broke her thoughts. It will be those exact same self-defeating broken thoughts that would prevent her from going on and living a more abundant life.

Cracker Barrel

Throughout the week, the young lady appeared to be in a continuous state of shock, discovery, and experiencing levels of epiphany. The week appeared to fly by. Early the following Saturday morning, we said our goodbyes, strategically packing the many suitcases and overnight bags into the back of the rented eight-passenger SUV. We were on the road for several hours before we decided to stop for a late lunch at Cracker Barrel. This was one of our favorite restaurants to visit when traveling, not to mention its roadside convenience. When we pulled into the restaurant's parking lot, Dot's demeanor immediately shifted from pleasantries to obnoxious. She was very adamant about eating at this particular restaurant. She strongly voiced her opinion that she did not, under any circumstances, desired to eat at this restaurant. It was late, everyone was hungry, and she was outvoted, so we all went in. Upon entering Dot's behavior once again drastically changed. She exhibited behaviors of cynicism, she also became off standish, quiet and withdrawn. When the waitress asked to take her order, she was blatantly rude, short, and overtly disrespectful. During the entire meal, she sat at the table with a blank, solemn expression on her face.

After everyone finished their meal and returned to the car, we asked her why she had such a negative attitude; not only with the waitress but throughout the entire meal. Still seething she blurted out, "I hate white people! "We asked her why and where all this was coming from? Her response was "I don't know, I just do." It was very obvious that she was upset and frustrated. She admitted that she had never dined at a Cracker Barrel restaurant before. She also admitted that she was very uncomfortable being around so many white people. On that particular day, there were only two African American families dining at the restaurant. Dot was more comfortable eating at establishments where the majority, if not all of the population were African Americans. She couldn't relax or return to her normal self until after several hours of driving. She became more relaxed as we approached the city limits. She actually took a deep breath and exhaled a sigh of relief as we drove closer to familiar areas, as we approached her neighborhood, and as we approached Dot's comfort zone, her brokenness was revealed on that road trip. I actually came to realize that her brokenness was highlighted after we had momentarily taken her out of her comfort zone, out of her immediate surroundings. I strongly believe that it was her displacement that revealed her brokenness. She was taken out of her comfort zone and placed in an environment that she had never experienced. She had never eaten at a restaurant where 98% of the patrons were Caucasian, and by doing so for the first time it exposed her brokenness.

Prejudice

I truly don't believe you are born prejudice, a bigot, or a racist. I believe we are taught these beliefs usually at an early age. These beliefs are then formulated into negative thoughts toward a person, a race, a group of people. Which will eventually manifest and be expressed in your words and behavior. If the people with whom you surround yourself with constantly encourage and support hatred of a particular group of people, most likely, and highly probable, so will you. It can occur gradually, and over a period of time, you can become comfortable with hatred. I met a young man many years ago who was very bitter. It was my freshman year of college. I believe this was the first year that the University implemented a co-ed floor. The room next door was occupied by two white male students. Once a week everyone on the floor was required to attend a mandatory floor meeting, in which everyone basically was encouraged to come together and share concerns, complaints, or highlights of their week. The two young men who shared a room next to mine would often arrive late to the weekly meetings. They would often position themselves in the back of the room, and they very seldom spoke a word. I also noticed that they did not speak to students of color; neither black or brown.

Throughout the semester I gradually observed a change in their behavior. While sitting within our group meeting, I noticed that they began to have brief conversations with my roommate and me. The weekly meetings created an opportunity for students to break off into smaller groups and to share their academic goals and experiences. These weekly meetings created an opportunity for everyone on the floor to get to know one another's personalities, likes, and dislikes. By the end of the semester, these two guys gradually became cordial, friendly, and polite. There were even times when we were able to share a pizza, a two-liter of Pepsi, and a joke or two. Before the end of the semester, we became good friends. One day, amid a conversation, which took place between the two young men, my roommate and myself, one of them brought up the subject of racism. One honestly and openly shared that prior to arriving on campus that he was a racist. He continued and went on to explain that when he discovered that two African American females would be living next door to him for at least the next two semesters he openly shared with my roommate and I that he hated us. He hated us only because of the color of our skin. He also shared that he hated us so much that he had planned to go home on the weekend, retrieve his gun, and bring it back to campus in order to kill us. He continued to share that that was his plan prior to getting to know us. He was raised within a predominantly white community and he attended a predominantly white high school. He also admitted that the majority of his friends and family members were prejudiced. This was his first- time experiencing living away from home, and living in a diverse community. And not to mention living in close proximity, and actually next door to someone of a different ethnic background.

The young man was able to push past his brokenness through his ability to step out of his comfort zone of hatred and prejudice. He developed the ability to become uncomfortable around individuals that he disliked, even despised. And by doing so, it created opportunities for him to connect with and honestly share and converse with individuals of a different color. By doing so he began to change his negative thoughts. He and I became close friends that semester. But suffice to say others in similar situations did not. Other students chose to remain in their brokenness. I wonder how many other broken freshmen set foot on that campus many years ago with a broken mindset of hatred and prejudice. I wonder how many remained throughout the course of their college education, only to graduate at the end of four years and not only leave with their degree but also leave with those same broken thoughts of hatred.

High Horse

As a young child, my mother would often encourage my siblings and me not to get "puffed up" or not to get "beside ourselves." It was also normal to hear her say, "don't start smelling yourself", or "you need to come down off your high horse." Mom had a way with words. It was her unique way of motivating her children to remain humble and not to be judgmental or look down on others who may be less fortunate. My mom used to always tell me don't look down on anyone to think that they are less than me because those same people you meet going up, you will meet coming down. In other words, she was basically trying to convey that the same people you meet on your journey to success you may also meet when you're going through hardship and difficulties. My mother was a constant reminder to be kind and respectful.

I recall years ago shopping with some friends; as we came out of the store a homeless man quickly approached and asked for some spare change. Although the homeless man was extremely polite and very respectful, one of my friends initially appeared extremely guarded and then removed. She immediately and loudly responded no to the man's request for money. As he moved in the opposite direction seeking to get the attention of another shopper my friend sighed with relief and glanced at him with disdain. At that moment she appeared to possess airs of eminence. Have you ever looked down upon someone who is less fortunate? Have you ever had degrading or belittling thoughts of the homeless, the needy, or possibly someone who is just down on their luck? These thoughts can often lead to feelings of superiority. We can become very comfortable thinking that way and there lies the endangerment. The danger of developing a mindset of entitlement, believing that you are more deserving or more worthy of money, position, or even power than the next person. Is it possible that you have become comfortable in the saddle of your high horse and worse not know it?

The Price Just Went Up

Continuous thoughts that lead to feelings of inadequacy, feeling less than, and feelings of not deserving, are broken thoughts. If you continue to harbor such thoughts it can lead to poor decisions and bad choices. Some time ago, a friend of mine went through a divorce. Roughly two weeks after the finalization of her divorce, two of her male co-workers approached her and informed her that the price had gone down now that she was divorced. She was confused and asked them to explain exactly what they meant. They went on to explain to her that since she was now divorced, she was less valuable and unworthy. Her co-workers boldly went on to blatantly inform her that she was used goods and that she should offer sex for free; with no strings or favors attached. She walked away from that conversation feeling embarrassed, hurt, and ashamed to be divorced. The weeks that followed were extremely stressful. As she replayed that conversation over in her head, feelings of disgrace, dishonor, and shame consumed her. Over a period of time, she actually began to believe her co-workers. She thought "the price went down" and she had begun to think she was less than. She even contemplated having random sex because she was now divorced and was undeserving of commitment and respect; though she thought. It was later in the week that she approached me and shared the conversation that took place between her and her co-workers. In a dejected voice she timidly asked me, "Mickey, when you get a divorce, does the price go down?" Without hesitation, I told her absolutely not, and I added, actually when you get a divorce the price goes up. She looked at me with raised brow with her eyes and mouth both wide open. She looked as if I had thrown a bucket of cold water in her face. I went on to explain to her how I became emotionally stronger and developed more positive mental thoughts after my divorce. I explained to her how traumatic my divorce was initially and how I refused never again to allow another man to mistreat me. I refuse to settle for nothing less than love. I now expect more, more love, care, and respect. I encouraged her that she is worthy and deserves to be treated with the utmost respect, whether married, single, or divorced. After a brief conversation, her self- esteem and confidence went up. Please never allow anyone to cause you to question your self-worth.

I Can't Go To College

A friend of mine shared with me a time when she went to visit her son's classroom. It was career day and the teacher discussed several career options and continuing one's education. At the end of the discussion the students were asked the following questions; what do you like most about school? What's your favorite subject? What do you want to be when you grow up? And do you think you would like to go to college? There were a variety of responses, but one little boy's response stood out. When the teacher asked the young boy if he thought he would like to go to college, he immediately responded no. He continued by saying there was no way he could go to college because his dad, his older brother, nor any of his uncles never went to college. He then asked the teacher what made her think that he could go to college? His teacher gave the basic response; if you work hard and put your mind to it you can do anything and that includes going to college. He said no I'm not smart enough; if my dad, my brother, and my uncles aren't smart enough to go to college, then I'm not smart enough either. His response left the teacher momentarily speechless. This young second grader believed that he was not smart enough to go to college because the men in his family had never gone. He assumed that the men in his family didn't further their education because they did not possess the intellect to do so. He thought if his family members were not smart enough, then surely neither was he. He was only seven years of age and possessed a strong belief that neither he nor his family members could ever pursue any form of higher education.

Truthful Lies

Truthful lies are false, misleading, and untrue statements that one may hear and even possibly repeat and share as sound truth. Truthful lies can also be false information that you repeatedly tell yourself. For example, an alcoholic, who may deny that they have a drinking problem. "I can stop whenever I want." "I'm only a social drinker." This is what the guy says with pockets full of breath mints and a trial-size bottle of mouthwash in the glove compartment of his car to mask the odor of alcohol on his breath. It is the same guy with a suspended license, three DUIs and a fifth of Bacardi wedged against the inside of the back of his toilet tank. He attempts to hide the bottle from his so-called nagging wife, who often tells him he has a drinking problem. With all the obvious evidence he still believes he does not have a drinking problem. Whether it's a lie someone told you or lies you tell yourself, if you accept and believe that lie to be true, then it becomes true to you. Have you unequivocally known something to be true, only to later second-guess yourself because of a repeated lie?

Lies are readily accepted as truth when they are constantly repeated, for example, stereotypes.

Racial stereotypes would be a perfect example. A stereotype is a general belief about a particular group of people, whether it is true or not. For example, the following are some stereotypes about different racial groups which have been accepted as truth, mainly because of constant repetition. The following are some typical stereotypes that are believed to be true: "All black people are lazy." "All white people are racist." "All Asians are smart." and "All Hispanics have three jobs." Although these statements are false, many believe them to be true. What other common false statements have you often heard and or possibly accepted as truth?

I Can Change Him; Not

I recall watching one of those nostalgic courtroom television shows, one which resembled an old Perry Mason rerun. The scene was set within a courtroom and the judge had just ruled that a young five-year-old boy be removed from his abusive home. As soon as the judge declared his verdict, the little boy leapt up from his seat, rushed across the courtroom, wrapped his arms tightly around his abusive fathers' leg, and began sobbing and screaming, "I love you, don't let them take me away daddy." As the father stood there with tears building in the corners of his eyes, and with a look of regret, he reassured his son that everything would be ok. He repeatedly told his son that he loved him as the bailiff pried the boy's ten small fingers away from his father's pants legs.

The least to say, it was a very moving and heart-wrenching scene. Although the young child was physically abused, when the opportunity presented itself to be released, free from his abuser he wanted to stay. Why is that? Why would anyone choose to live with an abusive individual? Why would you choose to live with an abusive individual when given the opportunity, to leave? Why is it that someone affected by domestic violence chooses to stay with someone who is abusing them? Or why is it that when they do leave, separate from their abusive partner or spouse they return? And often only to leave again and return again. This was the pattern, the routine of another very close friend of mine, who was also in an abusive relationship. Let's just say her name is Barb. Barb remained in an abusive relationship for roughly seven years. Her boyfriend was a heavy drinker and a drug addict. Within those seven years, I had often asked her why she just would not leave him. She would often respond, "I don't know." or "I love him." or what appeared to be her most common response, "He's actually a really nice guy when he's not drinking." I came to realize that all her reasoning and excuses kept her trapped within a comfort zone of abuse. And many years later I came to discover that so did mine. I had fallen into a conference zone of an abusive relationship and like Barb, I had developed similar excuses and reasons as to why I remained there within that toxic relationship.

Experts state that millions of individuals stay within abusive relationships for several reasons, ranging from finances, fear, guilt, love, religion, and many others. I experienced both verbal, mental, and physical abuse at the hands of my ex-husband. So why did I stay? I stayed because of some of the same reasons others stayed. I often thought and hoped that he would change. I thought I could change him. I thought that he would someday just stop, and no longer be abusive. I initially stayed because I loved him. That may very well be some of the same thoughts and reasons of an estimated 10 - 12 million other abused and broken people throughout the United States.

Reflection

It's critical to monitor our thoughts. Your thoughts have a great potential to influence the many areas of your life. Over time your broken thoughts will be expressed in broken words which can lead to broken behaviors which can lead to broken habits and ultimately result in a broken life. Even worse, those negative thoughts can create adverse feelings which in turn can create negative emotions, which can lead to stress, depression, and or sickness. Think about what you're thinking about, and just take time to think about your thoughts. Are your thoughts negative, judgmental, or hateful? I have lived and learned that your life will go in the direction of your dominant thoughts. Let me conclude this chapter with two of my favorite Bible verses; "Do not be conformed to this world, but be transformed by the renewal of your mind, that by testing you may discern what is the will of God, what is good and acceptable and perfect." , Romans 12:2 (ESV) "Finally, brothers, whatever is true, whatever is honorable, whatever is just, whatever is pure, whatever is lovely, whatever is commendable, if there is any excellence, if there is anything worthy of praise, think about these things." , Philippians 4:8 (ESV)

Chapter 4
Broken
Words

Introduction

Broken thoughts will eventually be expressed in broken words. Have you ever heard the following cliché? "Sticks and stones may break my bones, but words will never hurt me." That statement cannot be further from the truth. Words can hurt. Have you ever felt rejected, sad, lonely, depressed, or even in pain because someone hurled negative or even hateful words at you? If so, the odds are highly probable that you felt rejected or maybe downhearted. Broken words are individual words and or a group of words when strung together are considered rude, vulgar, disrespectful, or similar adjectives that may make individuals feel less than and possibly create self-defeating mindsets. Words incorrectly pronounced and incorrectly used within a sentence are also considered broken. We're often unaware, oblivious to the fact that we may have become comfortable speaking and or using our words incorrectly or in a demonstrative way. Some broken words have a tendency to misguide and misinform. Some examples of broken words are gossip, lies, slang, and PMUWs.

PMUWs are what I like to refer to as personalized made-up words. They are words that are often fabricated and initially shared amongst close friends and family members. Often these made-up words become commonplace and are routinely used and expressed in your daily conversations. Normally it's a word that's not found in the dictionary. If the word is found within the dictionary, it's not spoken or expressed with the same meaning. Some personalized made-up words are derived from mispronunciation. Often this may occur within your childhood. As a child, you may have heard your parents or your grandparents mispronounce a word then you may have mimicked those mispronounced words throughout your childhood and even possibly throughout your adult life. Now let me share with you some of my PMUWs which I discovered in my own adult life. For years I didn't realize that several of my words were broken. Over time my broken words became routine, comfortable, and commonplace.

"Finna"

I recall my first year of college. I was very excited about being out on my own, meeting new people, and having an opportunity to obtain a higher education. I was overall excited about learning. I recall one valuable lesson I learned it didn't take place within the classroom. It took place amongst a group of students, just standing around, hanging out in a common area. I learned that day that I had often used PUMW's (personalized made-up words). One of my classmates pointed out that I would often use the word finna; it was pronounced fin/na. Nearing the end of the group discussion, I stated, "I'm finna go." It was at that moment that another classmate immediately asked, "What is finna?" I responded, "You don't know what finna is? "He then responded, "No, I do not, and I have never heard the word before." I went on to explain and give the following examples; "I'm finna go to the store." "I'm finna go over there." or "I'm finna go to bed." I continued and explained to him that it meant that you were about to do something, or perform a certain action. My classmate stared at me bewildered and confused, as he stated that he truly did not believe that "finna" was an actual word. So, we looked the word up in the dictionary and to my surprise, it was not found. I thought it was an actual word because I had used it for years. I was very surprised that it was not in the dictionary and I thought to myself that "finna" did not exist. But it did exist. It existed within my household and my neighborhood. It existed in my community, in my church, and in my grammar and high school. I used the word "finna" on a regular basis. It was such a natural response. It was reinforced daily throughout my environment. I often heard my family, relatives, and friends speak this word continuously. Over the years that word was downloaded into my subconscious and after continuous repetition, I unconsciously became comfortable repeating this broken word. You might find it strange or incredulous that no one corrected or addressed my diction or poor choice of verb usage until I was in my late teens. Most likely they didn't recognize or identify finna as a PMUW. Or they possibly recognized the PMUW and for whatever reason didn't care to address it or bring it to my attention.

Sandwich

I once knew a man who is now possibly in his late 60s, and he once like myself, had become comfortable with his own PMUWs. I initially noticed on one or two occasions that he miss pronounced the word sandwich. Instead of saying sandwich, he would pronounce the word as sam/mitch. One particular day, he and I were talking within a small group of other individuals. Nearing the end of the group discussion he blurted out, "I'm hungry and I'm going to get my sammitch." he then proceeded toward the exit. Immediately after he left the room, muffled snickering sounds and low giggling tones filled the room. It was obvious that several individuals tried to hide their laughter. While others blatantly mocked and made fun of this man's pronunciation of the word sandwich. I did not find it at all humorous. I immediately sympathized with him because I knew what it felt like to be made fun of, and mocked because of using personalized made-up words or possibly one's inability to correctly pronounce a word.

I so vividly remember my freshman year of college. I can recall the many times when I used the word "finna" in several of my conversations. There were times when individuals stared at me in bewilderment as if I was speaking another language which in actuality, I was. Because of these reasons I felt compelled to speak to this man about his miss pronunciation of the word sandwich. So, I tactfully and respectfully approached the gentleman and explained to him that he mispronounced the word sandwich. My advice was not received kindly or with appreciation. His response was, "oh whatever!" I'm not quite sure if he was offended, embarrassed or if he just didn't care to know the correct pronunciation. Whatever his reasoning was, he continued to mispronounce the word sandwich. I have also heard others miss pronouncing the word shrimp as scripps. Many continue to do so because they are content and comfortable in doing so. On the other hand, others may not be aware that they are pronouncing it incorrectly. I get it, over the years I have observed many individuals who are aware of the fact that they are miss pronouncing the word but yet they continue to choose to do so. My mother would often say you can't teach an old dog, new tricks. My father often said that you can lead a horse to water but you can't make him drink. I have often heard many senior citizens, including my grandmother say, "I'm too old to try to change my ways now." In short, people usually become comfortable speaking a certain way and refuse to speak correctly. Unfortunately, they will remain there, using their broken words by choice. It's often difficult to indicate or identify your broken words simply because your friends and family members may also repeat the same broken words. When this occurs, it reinforces and encourages the usage of that broken word.

B or V

For several years I unconsciously became comfortable mispronouncing and or incorrectly enunciating certain words and letters. I especially mispronounced the letter V and the letter N. If the letter V or the letter N was positioned in the middle or near the end of a word, I would often pronounce it as the letter B or the letter M. For example, I would sometimes pronounce the word glove as glob, and the word phone as phom. Once I discovered these broken words, I made great attempts to eradicate them from my vocabulary. But I must admit that even today my children will sometimes point out the fact that I still unknowingly will inadvertently mispronounce the word glove and the word phone.

Baby Talk

The birth of a baby is so exciting. Parents and family members patiently watch the development of their babies. They eagerly watch each stage of the child's development. For example, when the baby is able to lift their head, roll over, scoot, crawl, walk, and say their first words. Many of the baby's first sounds resemble gibberish, coos, and ahhs. Over time the baby's words become recognizable. Some of the babies' first, commonly known spoken words are mama, dada, and no. Babies often attempt to mimic the sounds and words of the people often around them. Normally it's the parents or other family members. It's these same individuals who are unaware and unconscious of their baby talk and the effects it can have on the young child. Baby talk appears to occur naturally. It's just something about seeing an infant that causes individuals to instantly speak parentese. Baby talk is sometimes referred to as parentese or motherese, which is a type of speech where parents speak to children in an exaggerated and repetitive form of speech. It's when parents speak to their infants in high-pitched voices, along with slower rhythms and tones. Parentese is basically an infant-directed type of speech in comparison to an adult-directed type of speech.

It's now so commonplace to speak parentese to infants and young children. Research finds that it's spoken within most of our cultures and used across many languages; it's also expressed in sign language. The following are some distortions of words often used in baby talk: dolly substituted for doll, teensy-weensy instead of tiny, and twain for train. Because the young children attempt to mimic their parents, inadvertently they will also mimic the baby talk. Speaking to children this way may sound cute and sweet, but research shows that it may also slow down language development. Research and studies suggest that speaking complex sentences to young children may set a better example and improve their language. Have you become comfortable speaking baby talk? Are you even aware of your baby talk?

The N-Word

Another well-known and controversial word that I would like to include in the category of broken words is the N-word. The N-word is one of those words that does not have a middle ground; you're either on one side of the fence or the other. Many Individuals freely express themselves by using this word within their daily conversations without any revocations. However, on the other hand, many find it offensive and avoid using it. I must admit that there was a time in my life that I teetered on the fence about the usage of this word. Many years ago, I used the N-word in my daily conversations. That held true for several years until one day my youngest daughter, Delana asked to speak with me about something that was weighing heavily on her mind. She explained to me that she found the use of the N-word not only offensive but also degrading to our immediate family members and also to our African American community as a whole. My initial mental response, which I did not verbally express to her, was "What's the big deal?" At that time in my life, I was constantly using the N-word. Like many others, I had no problems, no remorse, guilt, or shame when I referred to myself and others as an N *****. Nevertheless, by the end of our conversation, my daughter had eloquently and emotionally expressed how she felt about the usage of this racial slur. I have to be honest; when she initially shared her concerns, I thought she was placing too much emphasis on the subject matter. I thought it was no big deal to use the N-word; I thought it was not that serious. But it was that serious. I had unconsciously become comfortable using this broken word.

As a child, I don't recall hearing and using this word as often as it is uttered today. Growing up, I recall both my parents and my sister often encouraging me to take pride in my black heritage. They encourage me to be proud of who I was as a black individual and always strive to do my best. They also encouraged me not to use the N-word because it had a great potential to create a mindset of inferiority. Over the years the N-word has become more tolerated, and readily acceptable. I have heard children as young as three use the N-word, and pronounce it with clarity. Times have truly changed, and after having that conversation with my daughter many years ago I knew that I also had to change. I think back and wonder what if she never had that conversation with me; would I still be using the N-word? I believe most likely I would. That conversation I had with my daughter had awakened me to a different level of thought.

Gossip

Do you often embellish the truth? Are you an individual who habitually reveals personal and private facts and or rumors about others? Are you known to share information that is damaging to one's reputation? Are you a gossiper? I have to admit there was a time in my life when I was consumed with the desire to gossip. I had fallen into a comfort zone of gossiping, especially within the workplace. Gossip is often routine and commonplace within the workplace. I hate to admit it, but I too had become consumed and comfortable with gossiping. Researchers suggest that roughly 80% of our general conversations are made up of gossip.

One day, for no particular reason, I decided to test to see how quickly rumors and gossip spread throughout the workplace. I initiated a rumor about myself. I shared with one individual in confidence that I was pregnant and asked them not to repeat this sensitive information to anyone. Unsurprisingly it was less than a week, probably within 2 to 3 days, that I noticed a change in several individuals' dispositions. It was the way they now spoke to me; it was also their facial expression and it was also the look in their eyes. I knew the rumors had begun to spread. Many of my co-workers relished the new gossip like a breath of fresh air. Within the weeks that followed, I estimated that approximately 90% of the entire staff knew fragments or distorted parts of the rumor. The months that followed were very interesting. It was quite entertaining to daily watch as several staff members guarded their conversations when they were around me. They made great attempts not to use certain words, such as the word baby, children, or other words relating to motherhood or pregnancy. I often observed co-workers initially look at me directly in my face and then quickly look down at my stomach in an attempt to see if there was a protrusion, a noticeable baby bump, or some indication of weight gain. They were searching for signs of pregnancy. By the end of roughly three-plus months, without no visible signs of pregnancy, I'm sure several staff members concluded that I had an abortion, which created fresh new rumors. As the rumors of "my so-called abortion" started to circulate, co-workers became uninterested and eagerly turned and targeted their attention on the next person of interest. As I now reflect back on that experiment and that case study, I realize there was no harm done due to the fact that the story was fabricated. Because I initiated the rumors about myself, I was not affected by the blank or smug stares, nor the whispers behind my back. But that was not the case for many others. Throughout the many years of my employment, I had observed co-workers suffer as they endured embarrassment, grief, hardship, and stress because of workplace rumors and gossip.

Lies

My mother often said, "If you tell one lie, you are going to have to tell another." She often encouraged us not to lie, and especially not to her. While growing up I quickly discovered this to be true. When people tell one lie, they will normally tell another one to cover up the first lie. I have also come to discover that if someone tells a lie often enough, then it has the potential to become true to whoever may be listening. When you become comfortable spreading lies and believing lies, then you are broken. I recall growing up, and like many children, I also lied. I initially lied to avoid spankings, punishment, and other forms of discipline. Very young children seem to naturally lie. For example, when a mother finds a trail of cookie crumbs leading to their child's bedroom, she might politely ask the child if they had been in the cookie jar. The majority of the time children would shake their heads vigorously from side to side with wide-open eyes and convincingly say no. The lies often continued into the child's teenage years. Let's see if some of the following questions sound familiar. Can you recall your parents asking the following questions; "Did you clean your room?" " Did you spend all your allowance in one day?" "Did you get in last night after your curfew?", "Did you use my car when I was out of town?"" Were you on that phone all night?" Do any of those questions sound familiar? If so, do you remember your answers? Did you lie to your parents? Are you still lying to your parents?

Those simple, routine lies often become habit-forming. I discovered in my teen years that lying or giving half-truths was often convenient, especially when dating. I recall thinking what's the big deal? It's just a little white lie, everybody lies, I'm not hurting anyone, and as long as I don't get caught, then it's ok. But it wasn't ok. I had begun to fall into a pattern, a comfort zone of telling lies. But I never considered myself a liar. A liar was someone who deliberately made untrue, false statements with the intent to deceive. That description seemed quite severe. Nevertheless, for many of my high school years that was often very descriptive of me. Several years ago, I was thumbing through my Bible and came across a Bible verse that instantly changed my outlook and perspective on lies and liars. It was in the book of Proverb 12:22. In summary, it reads that the Lord detests lying lips, but he delights in those who tell the truth. After reading this, it was as if something had awakened in me. My first thought was that I did not want God to hate me. I came to realize that although God hates sin, he loves us. Today I am no longer comfortable telling lies. I now practice keeping my mouth closed when tempted to say something that is not true.

OOW

Can you remember back to a time when you were young and purposely or accidentally said a curse word? Did everyone in the room immediately gasp and look shocked? Did anyone put their hand over their mouth or possibly shout, "OOW, you said a bad word!" Did you notice as you grew that your profanity became more acceptable? What happened over the years? Why is it that people no longer appear shocked when you now curse? Using curse words in our everyday vocabulary has become acceptable and commonplace. Profanity is broken words. They are often used in arguments, telling a joke, within one's basic rhetoric, or routinely within their day-to-day conversation. Oftentimes these words are used to highlight, emphasize or express a stronger meaning to what someone is trying to convey. Some of your basic, well-known, common curse words: s***, f***, D*** and so many variations of others. Out of all the words used as profanity, there is one curse word, and without fail, it always pulls at my heartstrings, every time I hear it. It bothers me when I hear someone say, "God d***." Out of all the curse words, I believe this one to be the most broken. It's so randomly spoken, and to many it's like a knee-jerk reaction. I truly don't believe many people don't realize the severity of uttering these words. When you shout out this statement accidentally or on purpose, you are literally dishonoring God, which is extremely broken.

Whining

Have you ever met anyone who constantly complains and whines about everything? Are you a pessimist? Do you constantly see or anticipate the worst outcome of a given problem? When faced with life challenges, do you gripe, complain, and only look at the negative sides of things. I get it; we all complain and sometimes whine in life. But then there are others who constantly complain and whine about everything, both negative and positive circumstances. It's as if nothing will please them. It's usually those individuals who always look at the cup as half empty instead of half full. And because of their pessimistic outlook on life, it's often reflected in their words.

Reflection

If you're not quite sure if you are using broken words, then ask someone. Ask friends and family members if your words make them perplexed, offended, hurt or simply uncomfortable. Pay close attention to individuals' facial expressions and even their body language when in a conversation with them. While you're speaking, do they appear interested and engaged, or are they withdrawn and apathetic? Sometimes this can be an indicator that you are using broken words. As you attempt to identify your broken words, be patient. I must admit that I'm still in the process of identifying, confronting, and correcting some broken words which unexpectedly emerge within my conversations. When this occurs, I immediately address and correct each word. My children have been a tremendous help in this area. My children and even now my grandchildren will notice, point out, and then assist and or correct me when I use broken words. Whether it's the use of PMUWs, profanity, a lie, gossiping, or similar broken words they are now more quickly addressed.

Chapter 5
Broken
Behavior

Introduction

Broken thoughts are often expressed or conveyed through your broken words and in turn, will eventually be expressed through broken behavior. Let me momentarily reflect on my childhood. As a young child growing up, I recall my parents being very influential. I adopted and mimicked many of their mannerisms, beliefs, values, and behaviors. I was greatly influenced not only by my parents but also by relatives, and close friends. They all had a great impact on my young life. They planted within me certain behavioral seeds, which began to take root and grow during my adolescence and adult life. Later in life, I discovered that I unconsciously repeated many of their behaviors both positive and negative. Is it possible that your family members, and/or others unknowingly influenced you with their negative behavior? Let me share with you some broken behaviors that I and others had become comfortable with. As you read, contemplate, and honestly consider if it is possible that you have fallen into identical or similar broken behaviors?

I Do / I Don't

I recall many years ago watching a late-night television show. It was a comedy show where two ladies who were best friends were talking about marriage. One of the ladies had recently married her longtime boyfriend. The now married lady stated that she was so happy because she can now "let herself go." She went on to explain that prior to getting married, she faithfully made sure that her hair and nails were done. The young lady always wore fashionable clothes. She also worked out on a daily basis in order to maintain her figure.

It was all in an attempt to get married, "to catch a man." Once married, she drastically changed. She seldom worked out, put on make-up or dressed up. My first response was that that's terrible, but when in actuality, I had acted similarly. I don't know exactly when it happened but shortly after my marriage, I also became lax in my physical appearance and attire. As I think back, I stopped working out as often as I once did. I remember a time at the beginning of my marriage when I used to wear lipstick all the time. I didn't notice that I had drifted away from just the simple act of applying lipstick. I had become comfortable with not getting my hair done regularly. I would often just throw on a cap. I fell into the habit of wearing a pair of blue jeans, gym shoes, and t-shirts. That had become my norm. I had slowly become comfortable neglecting my appearance. In my defense, I was working a full-time job, raising five children, running a household and attempting to be a supportive wife. Many women have shared with me that this can be very challenging, especially for moms who work full-time jobs and are attempting to raise young children. My mother happened to be one of those women.

My mother frequently encouraged my sister, and me to always act like a lady, and to keep ourselves neat and clean. I remember my mother taking pride in her appearance. I used to love to stand in the bathroom doorway and watch her as she put her makeup on. There was always a jar of ponds cold cream in reach. My mother had a routine when she applied her makeup. She would first evenly apply the cold cream in order to moisturize her skin. Then she would reach for her powder puff, and gently and evenly apply a thin layer of powder over her face. Lastly, she applied her bright red lipstick. Like many other young girls, I stood there in the doorway and thought that my mother was the prettiest mom in the world. As far back as I can remember my mother always took pride in her appearance and encouraged my sister and me to do the same. I honestly don't know when it happened but there was a space and time within my marriage when I had not given much attention to my attire or my overall appearance. I had fallen into a comfort zone of not dressing my best as often as I should have. It wasn't until after coming out of my comfort zone of a broken marriage that I was more inspired to dress up and pay closer attention to my attire. Have you said "I do", but now you don't?

Elderly Abuse

What comes to mind when your grandmother crosses your thoughts? Do you recall patiently and lovingly assisting her walking, possibly because she used a walker or maybe a cane? Can you remember her gray hair or the netted shawl draped around her shoulders in order to keep her warm? Maybe you can vividly remember her reading glasses which always seemed to be perfectly balanced on the tip of her nose? Maybe you can recall a precious moment baking cookies with your grandmother. And if so, did you get flour all over your hands and face? I remember many loving memories of my grandmother. She was very much loved and respected. Unfortunately, not everyone reveres and respects our senior citizens.

I recall about five years ago watching a young lady on the news as she shared many fond memories of her grandmother. But those memories were overshadowed by painful thoughts. The lady went on to explain how her almost 80-year-old grandmother was attacked and robbed. Everyone's eyes were glued to the television set as we intently watched the news coverage about senior abuse. On this particular day, I was in a public place, watching the news with about 25 other individuals. There was a young lady within the group, probably in her late twenties or early thirties. Everyone responded to the news coverage with shock and sympathy. But this one young lady responded quite differently. She shared with the group that many years ago she and her friends used to attack and rob senior citizens. It was incredulous! I could not believe what I was hearing. So, I looked her directly in her eyes and slowly asked her, "Are you telling me that you actually attacked and robbed a senior citizen?" Without hesitation she responded yes. Her yes response immediately pulled at my heartstrings. She noticed my appalled reaction and asked, "What's wrong with that?" She stated that the incident occurred over 10-15 years ago, and she added that she was very young at the time. With no emotions or regrets, she asked me, "Haven't you ever wanted to do something crazy when you were young?" I responded of course; when I was young, I snuck a cookie before dinner, I stayed up way past my bedtime, and even attempted to drink and smoke before I reached legal age. When I was young, those were some of the things I considered crazy. But it never crossed my mind to physically attack and rob anyone, especially a senior citizen. Even as she retold her story, there were no visible signs of regret or remorse. What made her think that was, ok? What initially led her into such a debilitating and horrific comfort zone of abuse and robbery? It appeared that it was all performed under the auspices that she was young and just wanted to do something crazy. Maybe it was peer pressure, and maybe she wanted to fit in with the wrong group of people. But it was obvious that she had become comfortable with repeated acts of abuse without a conscience.

I know this young lady had a father who she was very close to and whom she dearly loved and cared for. I asked her what if someone, just for fun, decides to grab, attack her father and forcefully take his possessions. She immediately became angry, defensive, and combative. She raised her voice and immediately stated, "that is my father, and don't nobody grab my father!" The young lady could not relate to the abused senior citizen in the same way she related to her father. I explained to the young lady that the old lady whom she attacked many years ago was most likely someone's mother, she was someone's grandmother and her children and grandchildren love her just as much as you love your father. She had a very difficult time comparing the two seniors, her father and the female senior citizen she had attacked and robbed many years ago. She had become comfortable with the ability to mistreat, hurt and rob one and love, respect and cherish the other.

9 to 5

Millions of individuals get up every Monday morning dreading having to go to work. Nevertheless, five days out of the week they reluctantly pull themselves out of bed, dress, and fight traffic in order to arrive at work. They often muster up enough physical and mental strength to make it through an eight, or sometimes a sixteen-hour workday. I once worked with this man who fell into a similar routine. His office hours were from 9 to 5. One day in passing he enthusiastically shouted out "I live for 5 o'clock!" Normally when someone made this statement I would just smile and not give it much attention. But this particular day when my coworker made this statement something was different. It was the look on this man's face and the tone in his voice that made me stop and give him my full attention. While glancing down at his watch, which read 4:57 PM, he stated that he had to go. He then turned and quickly walked away. I stood there momentarily as I watched him hurry down the hall, headed toward the exit. As he turned the corner and disappeared, I thought how sad. I thought how sad it was to start an eight-hour workday while continuously focusing on the last hour of the day. Unfortunately, millions of employees do exactly this. Many of us have fallen into a habit, a practice of going to a job we hate. Do you despise your job, and dread going into work each morning? Some statistics show that approximately 85% of employees hate their jobs, yet they continue to go every day. Each day they complained without making plans or taking steps to change their situation. Have you become comfortable going to a job you dislike?

Living On Line

I initially began to explore Facebook and other social media sites back in 2007. I was able to find and connect with old friends and long-lost family members. It was exciting to reconnect with new and old acquaintances. I began to explore several social medias; Facebook, Instagram, Pinterest, LinkedIn, and others. I found myself daily logging onto Facebook. I became very concerned after losing track of my time while scrolling through Instagram. One night I noticed I spent three uninterrupted hours on Facebook; that was out of the norm for me, and a bit too much. To be honest, it was quite disheartening. I had become frustrated because I had allowed myself to randomly scroll through individual posts, pictures, memes, and videos without monitoring my time.

I found myself investing several hours a day on these social media sites. I would randomly look at individuals' posts, give thumbs up, and send hearts and smiling faces while showing approval and agreement. Social media had begun to consume a great deal of my time, so I had decided to "fast" from social media. I removed, and deleted several social media apps from my phone, and it was truly freeing. The results were awakening and eye-opening. Logging off of social media for a few months revealed the actual amount of time I spent on Facebook. Now I understand that many individuals spend a large amount of time on social media to create informative and motivational YouTube videos, Instagram, and other avenues to build and monitor their brand and businesses. Nevertheless, we need to have balance. Many of us need to take an honest look at the amount of time we spend on social media.

"Telking"

For many years I had a pet peeve about watching television when eating dinner. I know it's because I was raised that way. As a young child, I remember my mom would always set the dinner table and we would sit down as a family and eat together without watching television. Mom would often remind us to use our inside voices, sit up straight, and keep our elbows off the table as we shared a meal and the events of our day. I often repeated these values when raising my children. My children can attest to this, especially during Sunday dinners. After church we would come home and immediately prepare to eat dinner. While eating, we did not turn on the television, or the radio, nor did I allow my children to talk on the phone. Years ago, many families would sit down, and share a meal and a conversation uninterrupted by any form of social media. Wow, how time has changed. Today everyone seems to be on different schedules and appears to be very busy. It's very seldom that we get to eat at the same time, and if so it's in front of a television with our plates in our laps, a fork in one hand, and our cellphones in the other.

I recall several years back, my two youngest children, Delana and Marcus and I was sitting at the table having a conversation when my son unexpectedly received a text. He quickly picked up his phone, briefly responded to the text, and then placed it back on the table. As we continued our conversation, my daughter's phone buzzed; it was a notification. She briefly picked up her phone, responded, and placed her cell phone back onto the table. Within the span of about 30 minutes, I noticed my children were no longer giving their undivided attention to the conversation. They were no longer interested in the table topic. They both had their heads down, looking at their phones. They were now both vigorously moving their fingers quickly across their cell phone screen. They were sending and receiving texts, responding to posts, checking on current news briefs, checking their Facebook status, and viewing other social media sites, and they were sharing their findings with each other through texts. They were, what I like to refer to as "telking." Telking occurs when there are two or more individuals in the same room, often in close proximity, possibly laughing, talking, holding a brief verbal conversation, and simultaneously texting each other with very little or no eye contact. I often observe this behavior more often when I'm out at a restaurant. Next time you're out at a restaurant, look around and count how many people are sharing a meal and "telking." I find that to be so disheartening; to be able to sit across the table from someone, not look at them, and only communicate with them through texting. Although telking is broken, it is becoming increasingly popular and acceptable.

I Can't Drive 55

When approaching an intersection and the traffic light turns yellow, do you speed up or slow down? When approaching a stop sign do you slow down, make a complete stop before proceeding, or do you slightly reduce your speed and drive past it? Do you drive the posted speed limit? Present-day, with the help of the red-light enforcement traffic light, I'm much more mindful of slowing down and coming to a complete stop at the intersection when the light is yellow. Several years ago, I was listening to the radio and I heard a song entitled "I can't drive 55". The band was conveying that they had a need to speed. The song clearly expressed the fact that many individuals are unable to drive the posted 55 miles per hour speed limit.

Some years back I was driving 35 mph in a 30mph speed zone and I was pulled over by a police officer. After he checked my license and registration, I asked the officer why he had pulled me over. He informed me that I was speeding. I politely informed him that I was very mindful of my speed, and I added that I was only driving 35. The officer pointed out that the posted speed limit was 30 and I was driving five miles over the speed limit. He went on to inform me that many drivers believe that there are five miles over the speed limit grace period. That is simply not true. Drivers have become comfortable driving five miles over the speed limit. If the truth is told many officers have become comfortable allowing drivers to do so. The police officer can actually ticket you for going one mile over the posted speed limit. I have observed individuals drive 20-30 miles over the speed limit within a residential area. Depending on the time of day and the weather, it is common to observe individuals driving 70-90 miles per hour on a 55mph posted highway. This occurs more often within the last left lane of many of our popular highways and expressways. This has become commonplace and increasingly acceptable. Great deal of drivers has become comfortable speeding, which is breaking the law. Do you drive the posted residential speed limit? Can you drive 55?

Spanking / Discipline

There are many points of view and several philosophies of how, or as to what is the best approach to discipline children. As I mentioned earlier, broken people break other people, and unfortunately that brokenness is often handed down generation after generation. This is also true as it relates to discipline. Today there are several different forms of discipline, ranging from the time- out method to spanking. My parents believed that physical punishment was an effective form of discipline. I believed the same.

I also used the same methods of discipline with my children that my parents used. My mother was the main disciplinarian; she did the majority of the spanking. Actually, my father never spanked me. My mother would often use a switch from a tree or an electric cord. When I became a mother, I disciplined my children with similar methods. Now you may think that a switch from a tree and an electric cord are harsh forms of punishment to inflict on a child. You can look at me and say I was mean, I was cruel, I was a bad parent, but you can also add, "I was broken." That was the major form of discipline I observed growing up. So as an adult that was the only form of punishment I knew to administer. I don't know when it occurred but at some point, I stopped using that form of discipline with my children. I now have grandchildren and I cannot fathom, nor ever imagine spanking them with a switch or an electric cord.

Somehow when parents become grandparents, they become softer, more patient, and more understanding of their grandchildren than they were with their children. I thank God that neither of my five children uses that form of discipline with my grandchildren.

Some older individuals have shared some of their childhood disciplinary experiences. A friend of mine once shared with me that his father would take him to their basement and ask him to remove all his clothes. His father would then tie him to a pole and spank him until he passed out. He shared that he would later wake up, dazed, and lying on the floor naked. A lady also once shared with me that her mother used to tie her to a chair before spanking her with an electric cord. I strongly believe these forms of discipline are extremely severe. These forms of discipline are broken and sadly enough, the brokenness is often passed down generation after generation, especially within my African American culture. I truly believe these harsh forms of discipline were handed down from our ancestors who were enslaved and brutally beaten at the hands of white slave owners. What form of discipline was handed down from your ancestors? Are you possibly unconsciously administering cruel and harsh discipline to your children because you were treated as such?

Good To The Last Drop

I recall as a child trying to get the last drop of ketchup out of the bottle. When the ketchup no longer flowed freely from the bottle, my siblings and I would add a small amount of water to the bottle, vigorously shake it up, and then turn the bottle upside down to allow the remaining ketchup to drain to the bottom. This would allow the last drop of ketchup to flow freely. This not only took place with the ketchup, but it was also a ritual we performed with all the condiments in the house. As an adult I found myself repeating the same broken habits; some of the same rituals which I performed in my childhood. As an adult, I could have simply retrieved another bottle from the refrigerator or grabbed one off the shelf before attempting to drain the first bottle. I recall my youngest brother Fred simply one day pointing out a full bottle of ketchup on the shelf as he reminded and encouraged me that we no longer have to add water to our almost empty ketchup bottles. He was absolutely right. I now had the finances and the option to just run out to the store and purchase another bottle. Today I no longer add water to my ketchup bottle in an attempt to retrieve every drop.

Shopping

When growing up I dreaded going grocery shopping with my mother. She had a routine and a unique way of shopping. When she entered the supermarket, she would immediately head straight to the discounted table which was full of overly ripe or bruised bananas, apples, and other fruits, and vegetables which of course were drastically marked down for a quick sale. She would also stop by the bakery, which also had a table of discounted, week-old bread and pastries. My mom had a strategic way of maneuvering herself throughout the store to first locate all the discounted stands or shelves which were often highlighted with bright orange or yellow neon poster boards with thick black letters and numbers announcing on any given day a 10% to 75% off sale. My siblings and I would patiently stand next to my mother at the discounted table praying and hoping that none of our classmates walked by and saw us. My mother would meticulously shuffle through dented cans, some without labels, and rewrapped damaged dry goods hoping to find the best deal. My mother was often on a fixed budget and she knew how to stretch a dollar. Over time both my parent's income had increased. Mom now had more money to shop with. No more dented cans or bruised fruit for us, so I thought. Although mother's income had increased and drastically changed, her shopping habits had not. For many years mom continued to shop for discounted groceries. My mother reminded me somewhat of "The Beverly Hillbillies." which was a 1970's sitcom that ran for many years.

The Beverly Hillbillies were a poor family who lived deep in the mountains. The father figure of the family was out hunting one day and struck oil and instantly he and his family became millionaires. They moved from a cramped, dilapidated shack to a spacious million-dollar home. Although their finances had drastically increased, they continue to possess a poverty mindset. Although they transitioned into a luxury home, they were complex and uncomfortable within their new lavish lifestyle. They continued to behave as if they were poor and as if they had limited income. They continued to drive the same car, wear the same clothes, and eat the same food which they were accustomed to. Their increased finances did not have a tremendous impact on their spending habits.

Sagging

I recall when my oldest son Terrence was in high school; although he never allowed his pants to sag below his waist, I was concerned because several of his friends did allow their pants to sag. To sag or sagging is a term often used to describe when an individual allows their pants to slightly or substantially fall below their waist and often reveals their underwear or undergarments. Over the years it has become a popular fashion statement. Today, within some communities, more than others, it's common to see our youth walking down the street with their pants below their waist. It may have stemmed from peer pressure or possibly just attempting to make a fashion statement. Peer pressure, fashion statement or not, I believe some of our children have taken sagging to another level. One day I witnessed a young man walking down the street and his pants were way below his waist. His pants rested slightly above his knees, making it very difficult for him to walk. I have never seen anything like this. I thought to myself that it would be simpler and quite easier for him to walk if he would just remove his pants and walk about with only his underwear on.

I met a young man many years ago and he was about the age of 15. He was in high school and had become involved with gangs and drugs which led to a drive-by shooting that almost cost him his life. He was shot and seriously injured. He explained to me the difficult time he had when he attempted to adjust from the life he once knew and now being paralyzed, incontinent, and confined to a wheelchair. Prior to being shot this young man would often walk around with his pants sagging. Although now confined to a wheelchair this young man continued to sag and expose his diaper. I inadvertently asked the young man one day if he realized that his diaper was showing and he confidently responded yes. I then asked him if he was sagging and he responded yes. He saw no reason to pull his pants up while in the wheelchair, as he saw no reason to pull his pants up when he had the use of his legs. Maybe he thought it was cool and or fashionable to sag, regardless if he was ambulatory or not. Maybe he didn't know that that act of pulling your pants off your waist and exposing your underwear was a behavior that is to be believed to have originated from our penal system.

Reflection

As you reflect back on this chapter, were there any ah-ha moments? Were you able to identify with similar broken behaviors? If not within your life, possibly within the life of others. Broken behaviors are basically habits and routines that you believe to be useful, beneficial, and possibly needed. With the passing of time, those same behaviors have a great potential to become dangerous, debilitating, and possibly detrimental. For example; the habit of overeating, if not monitored and curved, can affect your health. The habit of overeating and overindulgence can lead to increased weight gain and inadvertently lead to health problems, which can lead to a broken body. The same holds true for your finances. When you fall into a pattern of continuous overspending, it can lead to increased debt. A large amount of debt can have an adverse effect on your credit score and your purchasing power. Please note that broken behaviors are so subtle and if it's not identified they can prevent you from having the life you truly desire.

Chapter 6
Broken
Body

Introduction

You may ask what is a broken body and how can a broken body ever feel right? A broken body can occur when your body is not functioning at its optimum potential. It may be caused by nagging pain, chronic fatigue, a persistent headache, obesity, poor vision, hearing loss, mild to severe illness, or any other physical disability that prevents you from functioning at your optimal physical best. Many of these ailments prevent you from enjoying your life and striving to live your best life. So many things can break our bodies and not make us feel well; for example, drugs, both prescription and nonprescription, alcohol, stress, pollutants, and or a sedentary lifestyle. Whatever the case may be. Is it possible that you may have settled and accepted poor health as a way of life? Sometimes when we are in pain or discomfort for a long period of time, we tend to feel depressed and despondent. We often feel hopeless and tend to accept our current physical condition as permanent. We sometimes lose hope and believe it will always be like this and accept it as normal.

Is it possible that you have been experiencing pain or some form of discomfort for a given amount of time? And is it possible that you may have accepted this discomfort as a way of life? I often hear people say that when you get older you can expect your body to become weaker, possibly break a bone, gain weight, get on prescription drugs, develop heart problems, or other common diseases. This is the majority mass consensus of the world in which we live. Many of us have become comfortable with broken bodies.

MILDRED "MICKEY" GIVENS

Obesity

I remember my high school days; it was a time of discovery and excitement. I was very active and participated in different sporting activities which kept me slim and lean. I remained active even during my first year of college. Once engaged, unnoticeably at first, my weight slowly began to increase. I had fallen into a habit of overeating. I not only ate fast food on the weekend but also once or twice throughout the week. Whenever my children left food on their plates, instead of throwing it away I would often nibble off of each plate before washing the dishes. Marriage, raising my children, running a household, and working a full-time job made it very difficult to work out. As the years passed the weight continued to increase, but still, who had time to work out? That's what I used to frequently ask myself. Now I did some small form of exercise, but it was not enough to burn off the extra calories that I was consuming. Eventually, my stomach and waistline slowly protruded outward and forced me to use the last notch on my belt.

Every time I stood up from the table, I immediately took a deep breath and attempted to hold my stomach in, especially if I was out with friends and associates. Over time this became uncomfortable and unflattering. In an attempt to be more comfortable, I altogether removed the belt, which was only now hanging on by a thread. I stopped holding my stomach after each meal and I gave in and I bought the oversize T-shirts. No more neatly tucked shirts for me. I bought the next size up; I actually bought the next 2 to 3 sizes larger. It all depended on the cut and the style of the shirt. I eventually went up four pants sizes. Now wearing pants that actually fit my waist, I no longer attempted to hold my stomach in. I had now become accustomed to purchasing large and extra-large garments. It didn't happen overnight, but my body gradually transformed over months, even over the span of years. In June of 1979, I weighed 130 pounds. In June of 1990, I weighed almost 190 pounds. I roughly gained 60 pounds in eleven years. To look back on it now seems incredulous. It's difficult to believe that I had become comfortable with an extra 60 pounds of weight, but nevertheless, I did. I also found myself in a conference zone of obesity. I found myself living a sedentary lifestyle and had no desire to work out. I had fallen into a routine of constantly overeating and I had no revocations about it. I was overweight, sluggish, inactive, and broken. The sad truth is that many Americans have chosen a similar lifestyle. Statistics show that more than 1 in 3 U.S. adults are obese. Are you working out, eating right in an attempt to lose the extra pounds? Or have you just settled and become comfortable with the extra pounds? Have you become so comfortable that now the extra pounds don't concern you?

Prescription Drugs

Many years ago, I became comfortable with a sedentary lifestyle. I neglected eating right, working out, and making healthy life choices. These choices led to a decline in my health, which eventually led to a broken body. It was about twenty-plus years ago that I found myself extremely sick. I had fallen into a relaxed pattern of eating unhealthy foods and an inactive lifestyle. Which eventually affected my quality of life. Because I neglected my total well-being, I eventually found myself frail, weak and depleted with a compromised immune system. Neglecting my health caused me to daily consume several prescription pills in an attempt to create some form of balance within my body in order to perform simple daily routines. It seemed as if my doctor was writing me out a prescription on a regular basis. Over time, I found myself taking 32 pills a day. That was my regiment on a daily basis for years. I reflect back to when my pharmacist would give me precise details on how to take each medication. He would clearly state, "take two of these three times a day, take three of these, every morning, four of these, every eight hours, take this pill twice before you go to bed with food, and take this little white pill as needed. The list of directions was endless.

Over time the many different medications eventually eliminated most of my discomfort and pain. It also created a stable balance within my body, which allowed me to return to some form of normalcy. Inadvertently the pills also created a dependency. I needed and depended on the pills on a daily basis in order to manage pain and regulate the function of some of my major organs. And I was ok with that. Until one day my doctor informed me that the prescription drugs that I had been taking over a span of several years had the potential to create an adverse effect on my kidneys. It was at that moment that I made up my mind to begin taking better care of myself and not solely rely on prescription drugs. Working closely with my doctor, I decided to create a daily workout routine, make better healthy food choices, and increase my water intake as I attempted to wean myself off of all my medications. Unconsciously I had become comfortable taking a handful of pills on a daily basis. Presently today I'm very mindful of working out and maintaining a healthy weight and a healthy body. I am a totally different person from twenty-plus years ago. I am no longer on prescription drugs. My body is much stronger and healthier which allows me to live a more pain-free life and a more active lifestyle. None of this would have been possible if I had remained in that comfort zone of consuming an abundant amount of prescription drugs.

Bag Lady

Many Americans have settled and decided to live within a broken body. Today many individuals, once like myself, consume several prescription drugs. One study showed that nearly 70% of Americans are on prescription drugs. Many individuals remain on their medication without investigating or looking into alternative ways to improve one's health. I knew a lady who had been on prescription drugs for many years. Over the years she had developed a broken body and had become comfortable with it. But unlike myself, I truly believe that she had no desire to take the appropriate steps to improve her health. Not only did she become comfortable with her broken body, but she also exhibited attention- seeking behaviors. Her friends and family members had given her the nickname "bag lady." The nickname was quite befitting. She would often carry with her a large Ziploc sandwich bag full of prescription bottles, antacids, ibuprofen, and other pain relievers.

It was normal for her to literally empty the entire contents of the bag onto a table, line the bottles up, and briefly describe each prescription drug. After explaining each prescription, the dosage, and its side effects, she would immediately share the results from her most recent doctor visits. She shared detailed information about her blood work, cholesterol levels, and other personal medical information. Debra continued this ritual for many years. Now by all means, I am not being insensitive toward Debra or individuals who take prescription drugs on a regular basis. I am not saying that Debra didn't have physical ailments that required her to take medication.

But I pose the question; is it possible that Debra or possibly you or someone you know have become comfortable consuming prescription drugs that over the years may have created a broken body. All because of their need for attention? Just food for thought.

Headache

Do you experience persistent headaches? Do you find yourself constantly purchasing over the counter pain relievers? Well, several years ago I did. I recall a time when I routinely experienced throbbing and irritating headaches. Nowadays, I am not really a coupon clipper, but I remember a time I would search the weekly newspaper for discounted coupons for pain relievers. Excedrin, Tylenol, and similar pain relievers lined the shelves of my kitchen cabinet as well as my bathroom vanity and the top drawers of my nightstand. On average, I consumed 2 to 4 pain relievers every 4 to 8 hours in an attempt to alleviate my headaches, which range from mild, painfully irritating, and massive. Over the years I had come to only manage the pain. I realized that the many pain relievers I consumed were not a cure; they only provided temporary comfort. I fell into a habit of daily popping pain relievers in an attempt to manage the headaches.

Due to the constant frequency of headaches, I had begun to accept the pain and my pain management routine as a way of life. I didn't realize that the persistent headaches were not normal. I had become comfortable feeling uncomfortable. Fortunately, one day I shared with a friend that I was having frequent headaches. They immediately asked me if I regularly drink water and if so, how much? I had to admit that I did not drink much water and, on many days, I would not drink any water. On the other hand, I was consuming anywhere from 4 to 7 cans of pop a day. My friend went on to explain the possible correlation between the amount of water I drank and my painful headaches. She added that a lack of water can cause dehydration which can lead to headaches. I thought If simply increasing my water intake has the potential to eliminate headaches, then I was willing to try, and try I did. Not long after, I began to notice I was taking fewer pain relievers a day. As I continued to increase the amount of water I drank, I noticed that I experienced fewer headaches. Long story short, today I am very mindful of my water intake. I make great attempts to drink at least eight cups of water a day. Within the past year or so, I have only had one headache and I attribute that to the amount of water I now drink on a daily basis in addition to other healthy life choices.

Charley Horse

A charley horse is another name for an involuntary contraction of one's muscles; it's basically a cramp. For several years I suffered from painful leg cramps. It would sometimes occur throughout the day, which was not very painful; they were often tolerable. If the leg cramp occurred while sitting or standing, I basically stretched my leg until the tight muscles relaxed. Now on the other hand, the leg cramps that I experienced during the night were more severe; they were excruciating. The cramps were so painful that they would often wake me up out of my sleep. It felt as if a vice-like grip was clamped to the lower back part of my leg and with the slightest movement, the pressure would build. The agonizing pain would bring tears to my eyes and cause me to scream out into my dark bedroom in hopes that someone in a nearby room would hear my desperate call for help. If no one immediately came I would arduously rub the back of my leg for what seemed like an eternity before my muscle relaxed, which caused the pain to subside. For many years this had become a routine and a way of life for me. That is until a friend once again shared with me the importance of hydration. The simple act of increasing my water intake eliminated muscle strains, in addition to other physical ailments.

BM

Initially, I was going to leave this section out. But let's talk about bowel movements (BM). Not having regular bowel movements is a huge indicator that your body is not in balance. The inability to move your bowels and eliminate waste on a regular basis can create toxicity within the body. Several years ago, I recalled having one bowel movement a week. Maybe you are thinking, what's wrong with that? If you are currently eliminating once a week, then you may be experiencing bloating, cramping, flatulence, or other common stomach ailments. Some studies show that on the average people poop between three times a day to three times a week. In addition to having one bowel movement a week, I was also gassy and oftentimes uncomfortable. Because I had lived this way for so long, I thought this was normal. It was far from normal. If you have become comfortable pooping only once a week this can possibly lead to severe stomach issues. Some simple changes in one's diet have the potential to eliminate stomach discomfort and create regular bowel movements.

I Can See Clearly Now

I have worn glasses my entire adult life. My glasses allow me to see clearly, bringing items into focus. I'm nearsighted, which basically means I'm able to clearly see and focus on objects that are close or positioned only a few feet away. It feels as though I have been wearing glasses forever, but I initially started wearing them in grammar school, maybe in fourth or fifth grade. While in grammar school, I would often ask my teacher if I could sit in the front of the classroom because I was unable to clearly see the board. Some teachers were able to make accommodations, but unfortunately many were not.

I recall many days sitting in the back of my classroom and feeling extremely frustrated because I was unable to make out the words on the board. This often made it difficult to grasp and understand the lesson being taught that day. Over the years I had fallen into a habit of rubbing my eyes, blinking, and squinting in an attempt to bring objects into focus. For most of my young childhood, I viewed the world out of focus, blurred and obscured. Unknowingly I had become comfortable with poor vision. I had an obscure vision of the world around me. My broken eyesight felt right because I had nothing to compare it to. That is until the day I received my first pair of glasses. I vividly remember that day, it was amazing and it was life-changing. Immediately stepping outside the obstetrician's office with my new glasses perfectly positioned and fitted to my face, I gasped. My world had become crystal clear. Colors appeared to come to life; red, yellow, orange, and blue flowers appeared to leap out at me. The grass no longer appeared to be the shape of a large green blob or a huge green square. I was now able to see each blade of grass. I stopped and stared at the leaves on the tree. I was now able to see the delicate shape of each leaf, even the small veins that ran throughout the leaf. Lastly, I remember the sky; I felt as if I could reach up and touch it and I believe I attempted to do so. Now, this was the same beautiful bright blue sky that I had walked under for years, but it went unnoticed because my vision was obscured and blurred its true brilliance. It was as if I was living in a thin fog; prior to getting my first pair of glasses. Over the years I had become comfortable with that foggy vantage point. I didn't know that there was a beautiful clear world around me waiting to be discovered. I only needed to take a simple eye test. What are you not seeing? Have you been postponing a visit to your ophthalmologist? Have you become comfortable with poor vision and not know it?

False Pregnancy

What I believe to be another interesting example of a broken body is pseudocyesis, which is more commonly known as false pregnancy. Pseudocyesis occurs when a woman believes that she is pregnant when in reality, she is not. A woman with pseudocyesis may exhibit many if not all the signs of actually being pregnant but without the fetus. When a woman possesses a great desire, feelings, and thoughts of being pregnant, then her body has the ability to create symptoms as such. Some doctors believe that psychological factors may trick the body into thinking that it's pregnant. The woman's brain then misinterprets those signals as pregnancy and triggers the release of hormones such as estrogen and prolactin that leads to actual pregnancy symptoms, which creates a broken body. A woman who may be experiencing a false pregnancy can have many of the same symptoms as a woman who is actually pregnant. Research shows that the mind can prompt the body to produce believable signs of conception. Those symptoms may include nausea, vomiting, the interruption of one's menstrual period, enlarged breasts, milk production, weight gain, and even labor pains.

You may wonder if there is a cure for pseudocyesis? Well, it's not as simple as telling a patient who is experiencing a false pregnancy that she is not pregnant. Some doctors believe that it's better not to insist that the patient isn't pregnant but to simply present her with the lab findings and allow her to gradually come to the correct conclusion. Doctors may also offer therapy and emotional support. Even when presented with the lab findings, it's not uncommon for some women to reject their negative lab results and seek a second or third medical opinion. Many pseudocyesis patients can experience feelings and signs of pregnancy not only for weeks and months but also for years. Now that's a long time to maintain a broken body. That's a long time to feel right when your body is actually broken.

Birds Of A Feather Stick Together

I recall several years ago reading an interesting article in a health magazine. I often share this story because it's a great example of the human will and the ability of one man to drastically transform his broken body. The article was centered on a loving couple who had been married for several years. They were both approaching retirement age and looking forward to it. Unfortunately, tragedy struck, and their life and their retirement plan drastically changed. The wife unexpectedly had a heart attack and a mild stroke. In addition to other medical complications, she became very weak and was no longer able to walk or physically care for herself. She was heartbroken as she faced the reality of the possibility that she may be confined to a wheelchair for the rest of her life. Although her husband was devastated, he was also determined to do everything he could to provide his wife with the best possible care. The only dilemma was that the husband was not in the best health to provide the type of personal care that his wife required.

Before his wife became sick, the couple had similar health issues. They were "two birds of a feather." They were both overweight with high blood pressure and borderline diabetic. The husband considered these facts and knew he could end up like his wife or worse. He considered the possibility that if he became sick, he would not be able to care for his wife and possibly himself. So, he made a decision to change his eating habits and his overall lifestyle. He started working out, lifting weights and making healthy food choices. Over a period of time, he lost roughly a hundred pounds. He transformed his body from one of weakness, obesity, stiffness and aching joints to a strong, firm, tone and muscular sculptured body. He possessed the energy of a man half his age. He had so drastically changed his physical physique that several of his family members did not recognize him. His love for his wife and his great desire to care for her motivated him to lose weight and improve his health. His wife's untimely illness had created an urgency to exercise and get in shape. He felt as though he had been awakened from a stupor, a lethargic lifestyle. Prior to his wife becoming ill, he had no desire to lose weight, nor eat healthy foods. He had become comfortable with obesity, poor health, and a sedentary life.

Real Men Don't Go To Doctors

I know a young man; let's call him Jim. Jim absolutely refuses to go to the doctor unless, of course, there are extreme physical circumstances that possibly may lead to a medical emergency. He has informed me on several occasions that he has a high pain tolerance. That was his way of saying that he can tough it out. Jim uses his high tolerance for pain as an excuse and or a reason for not seeking medical attention. I often wondered why he would tolerate or even suffer from pain when he could possibly eliminate the pain by simply going to the doctor. I asked him why is it that he, and men in general, will suffer in silence and refuse to visit their doctor? He stated that he believes it's a waste of time, and he added there is also the fear factor that something may seriously be wrong. He concluded that he honestly prefers not to know. Some experts would agree with Jim. Research shows that Jim falls into the category of men which is very common today. Some statistics show that 31% of men only go to the doctors if they are extremely sick. 10% of men do not go to the doctor because they are afraid that something may seriously be wrong. Like Jim, 7% of men did not go to the doctor because they felt as though they didn't have the time. The constant avoidance of doctor visits can create a conference zone of living with pain and discomfort. Many of our fathers, husbands, brothers and sons have become comfortable while silently suffering. Have you become comfortable with suffering, with pain in your body simply because you refuse to visit your doctor? Now it's one thing not to be able to seek out medical attention because of financial hardship but to suffer from pain because of one's macho, manly ego is another matter; it's broken.

Reflections

Have you become comfortable with aches and pains and discomfort? Are you overweight, fatigued, and or constantly feeling tired?

Seriously ask yourself if you have become comfortable feeling uncomfortable? Is it possible that you have learned to live with, ignore, or possibly just endure pain and discomfort? Is it possible that you have become comfortable with a broken body? I did. It was the beginning of the year 2000, and I became extremely ill. After consuming a regimen of pain pills over several months with very little relief, I became discouraged. I started to believe that this was my lot in life: weak, depleted, frail, and dependent on others. The aches and pains appeared to last forever. Overtime I allowed myself to become comfortable with discomfort.

Due to a favorable and unexpected chain of events, my health slowly improved. I started to look into vitamins, nutrition, and different forms of physical activities. Over the years I have become more mindful of my physical and mental health. I no longer take either of them for granted. I have even reached a point in my life where I now monitor my health on a daily basis. When I wake up each morning, I'm very mindful and focused on my health and my overall well-being. Upon awakening, I quickly become in tune with my mental and physical state of being. If I'm not feeling my best or thinking positive thoughts then I immediately address it and set in motion a plan of attack to correct whatever may be out of alignment. I sometimes may have to decrease my workload and or increase my exercise routine. I may have to increase my water intake or adjust my meal plan. I may simply need to meditate, pray and find ways to laugh, and connect with loved ones, and other positive and supportive individuals. Whatever I may need at that moment to improve my mental and physical state I immediately move in that direction. I have discovered that these habits have the potential to prevent or lessen the chances of you becoming comfortable with a broken body.

Chapter 7
Broken
Finances

Introduction

What does it mean to be financially broken? Let's first describe what it means to be financially secure. Financial security is the ability to create, possess and maintain a multiple, steady stream of abundant amounts of income. Do you possess abundant or adequate financial amounts of monthly income? Is your monthly income greater than your monthly bills? Do you possess enough income to meet your daily, monthly, and yearly needs and wants? Or is it possible that you possess a large amount of debt? Are you in constant need or living a life of lack? Have you settled and become financially comfortable with barely getting by? If this has become a constant way of life for you, then your finances are broken.

I recall several years ago when my finances were extremely broken; I possessed a large amount of debt, I didn't have any savings, I did not have a budget, nor did I have the knowledge or know-how to correct it all. If you are experiencing any of these scenarios on a continuous basis then it's highly probable that your finances are broken. Statistics show that a large portion of our population has done just that. Let's pinpoint some possible broken finances. The following are some scenarios of broken finances that actually occurred in my life and the life of close friends. Let's see if you can directly or indirectly relate any of the following areas to your finances

Co- Sign

Co-signing is agreeing to pay someone's debt in the event that the responsible person fails to adhere to their financial obligations.

Have you ever cosigned for someone and only months later found yourself responsible for repaying a friend's loan; I cannot imagine. Many years ago, people would randomly ask to borrow money and never pay it back. This occurred more than I would like to admit. Nevertheless, it was then that I decided never to co-sign for anyone, not even my children. A friend of mine strongly begged to differ. That is of course until she found herself repaying her daughter's loans. My friend shared with me that she co-signed for her daughter to obtain a loan from the bank twice. Unfortunately, her daughter defaulted on both loans. Her mother struggled for months to repay each loan plus interest. To add insult to injury, the daughter made no attempts to repay her mother

As a parent, I know what it's like to want to give your children a head- start in life. If you are a parent of an adult child, it is highly probable that at least once you have offered them financial support. Maybe you assisted them with the down payment on their first home, helped them purchase a car, paid off some of their credit card debt, or offered to co-sign for them. And I get it, they are your children and you want to help. Most parents want to help their children succeed and that's understandable. But what I cannot understand is that, parents offer financial assistance when the parents themselves are experiencing financial hardship. If continuing to lend money and co-signing for someone else's debt creates a financial burden and hardship for you, then I would consider that financially broken. Let me end this section with the following Bible verse: "There's danger in putting up security for a stranger's debt; it's safer not to guarantee another person's debt." Proverb 11:15 (NIV)

Easy Come, Easy Go

Do you know someone who never seems to be able to hold on to a dollar? Do you know someone who is constantly broke and borrowing money? They may have a job and a steady stream of income, but they lack the mindset to manage their money. Do they spend every penny they get their hands on? Do you know of such a person or could that possibly describe you? If that happens to be you, then you're not alone. Millions of individuals have fallen into the habit of overspending. There are case studies revealing how individuals have won the lottery or may have been awarded an inheritance in amounts of hundreds of thousands of dollars. Money that had the potential to last a lifetime. Unfortunately, after only a couple of years or so the money has all been spent. Continuous overspending depletes one's savings and creates large amounts of debt. Why is it so easy for individuals to run through money and spend every dollar they make? You may say it's the lack of self-discipline. Yes, I agree, but in addition to a lack of self-discipline, I strongly believe people have simply become comfortable with overspending and possibly not know it.

Borrow

In my younger days, I would often lend out money, hoping they would return the money on the day they had promised to do so. People have asked to borrow money and promised to pay it back which they never did. In my younger days, that used to cause me to become frustrated and angry, which often created a wedge between myself and the borrower. The act of borrowing money and not wanting to or not being able to pay it back has separated the best of friends and divided families. I understand that life happens and sometimes we may need some form of financial assistance, and borrowing money may be our only option. I truly believe that most people, most of the time, have good intentions of paying the money back.

Many individuals are living paycheck to paycheck. We have become comfortable borrowing money to tide us over, and truth be told we have become comfortable with not giving money back that we borrowed. Some individuals have become so comfortable borrowing that it becomes part of their budget. Instead of living within one's budget, individuals attempt to budget and factor other people's money into their own personal budget. I know a young lady who currently doesn't have a steady job, but she has several friends who are more than willing to assist her financially. Her friends often assist her in paying her rent, maintaining her car, paying bills, and other daily living expenses. Over a period of time, she had become extremely comfortable borrowing money on a monthly basis. Is it possible that you have become comfortable borrowing, bartering, or even borderline begging? I do understand that we might need a couple of bucks to carry us through the week or something to tide us over to our next paycheck. But when you are constantly asking individuals for money on a regular basis this may be an indication that there is a crack or breaking in your finances. Scripture states that the borrower is a slave to the lender. Are you enslaved to someone because you owe them money? Let me close this section with the following Bible verse, "Owe no one anything except to love one another, for he who loves another has fulfilled the law.", Romans 13:8 (NKJV)

Public Aid

Let me first say, "a hand out is not always a hand up." Sometimes a donation or a monetary gift can do more harm than help. I have heard stories where there are second, third, and even fourth-generation families on some form of government assistance. In my heart of hearts, I believe something is wrong with that, but there are many who believe this to be normal. Now I will be the first one to admit that sometimes we may need some form of government assistance. Now if you are a third or fourth generation currently receiving public aid, then consider the possibility that you have become comfortable depending on public aid? I did. I remember when I became pregnant with my first child, and I was neither physically, emotionally nor financially ready. Ready or not, in a frame time of nine months I was about to birth into this world a child. He needed milk, food, pampers, and medical care. At that time in my life, I was simply unable to provide all these things for my son without financial assistance. So, I applied for and began to receive public assistance. The extra money immediately lifted many financial burdens. Over time the extra monthly money I received from public aid created feelings of contentment and ironically, a sense of expectation and entitlement. It wasn't until years later that I decided to return to school to obtain my degree in hopes of securing a more worthwhile job. Shortly after obtaining my degree, I was able to secure a job that drastically increased my finances. Financial security allowed me to support myself and my family without the assistance of public aid. Unfortunately, this was not the dream or goal of many other individuals who depended on financial assistance.

I once knew a young lady who was a second-generation public aid recipient. At that time, she had been on public aid for several years. She was very young, still in her early twenties with two children. Before the end of the year, she was once again pregnant. She was now a single mom with two young children and one on the way. My first thought was that the last baby was an accidental pregnancy; maybe she wasn't careful or cautious. But no, that was not the case. She intentionally became pregnant. She informed me that she planned to get pregnant, knowing that public aid would increase her monthly income. I was shocked, I could not fathom anyone doing such an extreme and calculated act. I could not imagine purposefully getting pregnant, bringing a child into this world, in addition to all the responsibilities of raising that child, only for the sole purpose of receiving a few more dollars each month. That occurred many years ago but I can now understand how this young lady was able to do this. I believe she unconsciously became broken. Over the years she had become comfortable receiving government assistance. Unfortunately, she raised her children for many years on public assistance. Let me end this section with the following Bible verse; "A good person leaves an inheritance for their children's children." (Proverbs 13:22) Your children and grandchild's inheritance should not be a link card or food stamps. When your finances are constantly broken it creates the likelihood that your next generation's finances will also be broken.

Put Your Oxygen Mask On First

Whenever we board an airplane and before we take off the flight attendant often gives instructions on safety rules. Parents are often reminded in case of an emergency to always put their oxygen masks on first before assisting their children. In spite of the fact that some parents may find this extremely difficult to do, I believe it's very wise advice. I believe this advice is not only befitting in emergency situations that may occur on a plane, but it can also be applied to emergency situations relating to one's finances. Children sometimes find themselves in emergency situations and in need of financial support. They will often elicit help from their father or mother. And oftentimes parents will attempt to go out of their way to assist. I want to encourage parents to first secure their personal finances before assisting their children with their financial needs and emergencies. In general, it's a good rule of thumb to apply this to not only our children but also to other family members and friends. Be mindful of giving financial support when you yourself are not financially stable, secure, or even capable. Over the years I have met parents who have given their children moderate to large amounts of cash, cars, homes, and credit cards. There are others who have paid off their family members' loans and other debts. Now please hear me and understand that I truly believe that it is admirable and a kind gesture to offer financial support to loved ones and friends in need. Now if you're financially secure and have a desire to help then by all means do so. On the other hand, if the act of lending money, co-signing, and taking on the responsibilities of others' debt may create a burden and financial hardship, then don't do it. We often allow our emotions to overrule our common sense. I had known individuals who had taken out a loan and given it to someone else when they themselves were in need.

A longtime friend had a son in college. Her son worked very hard and in spite of the odds against him, he made good grades, graduated, and secured a lucrative job. His entire family was extremely proud. But no one was as proud of him as his mother. Shortly after graduation, the young man asked his mother to put a large down payment toward the purchase of a new car in order to get back and forth to his new job. Her son had promised to pay her back when he started receiving regular and steady checks. His mother did not hesitate to do so. She withdrew most of her savings and applied it to the down payment of the purchase of her son's new car. She did so in spite of the fact that she desperately needed a new car herself. After several months the young man started to complain that he needed more living space. It was roughly within a year and a half after this young man graduated that he had purchased and furnished his first home but not of course without the financial assistance of his mother. Unfortunately, the young man never attempted to pay his mother back.

Credit Cards

Some years ago, I unexpectedly found myself in a large amount of credit card debt. I roughly had accumulated a total of $10,000 in debt. Honestly, I can't explain how it happened. I could barely remember the items I had purchased. The debt seemed to have occurred miraculously overnight. At least that's what I told myself. But I knew my debt had spiraled out of control over a period of several months. I had fallen into a pattern of impulse spending, paying the minimum monthly balance, and ignoring calls from my creditors. Poor spending habits, not using my credit cards wisely, and high-interest rates lead to a drastic drop in my credit score. This had adversely affected both my finances and my mental state. Debt can be both draining and stressful.

We often look at credit cards as free money. Not realizing that the so-called free money which you used at the beginning of the month can become a ball and chain by the end of the month. I definitely felt in bondage to my credit card debt. That feeling of being in bondage increased my level of stress. I attributed it all to the fact that I did not know how to use credit cards correctly. So, I reached out to someone who did. I called a longtime friend who was business-oriented and financially stable. She shared with me some practical step-by-step ways to get out of debt. I followed her advice and over time I was able to eliminate a substantial amount of debt. I went on to investigate other techniques as to how to not only eliminate "bad debt" but also how to manage "good debt."

Reflection

"If you have one penny, save half of it." I fondly remember this financial advice that my mother often shared with me many years ago. That was her way of telling my siblings and me to be frugal and not to overspend. My mother was very thrifty and she had the ability to stretch a dollar. I was extremely grateful for her advice but the fast-paced world that I grew up in had drastically changed. I discovered that I needed to know more than how to save and stretch a dollar. I also needed to know how to invest, trade, diversify and grow my dollars. There was so much to learn. Paul, a long- time friend of mine and other financial advisors shared with me how to create multiple streams of income. This was all new to me. But actually, it was not because most of their financial advice was biblically based.

Let me end this section with a suitable Bible verse. "Be sure you know the condition of your flocks, give careful attention to your herds; for riches do not endure forever, and a crown is not secure for all generations. When the hay is removed and new growth appears and the grass from the hills is gathered in, the lambs will provide you with clothing, and the goats with the price of a field. You will have plenty of goats' milk to feed your family and to nourish your female servants." , Proverbs 27:23-27 (NIV) The following Bible verse gives advice on how to invest; "Ship your grain across the sea; after many days you may receive a return. Invest in seven ventures, yes, in eight; you do not know what disaster may come upon the land. If clouds are full of water, they pour rain on the earth. Whether a tree falls to the south or to the north, in the place where it falls, there it will lie. Whoever watches the wind will not plant; whoever looks at the clouds will not reap. As you do not know the path of the wind, or how the body is formed in a mother's womb, so you cannot understand the work of God, the Maker of all things. Sow your seed in the morning, and at evening let your hands not be idle, for you do not know which will succeed, whether this or that, or whether both will do equally well." (Ecclesiastes 11:1-6 NIV) These are only a few of my favorite Bible verses relating to money. The Bible offers a wealth of information on how to avoid broken finances.

Chapter 8
Spiritually
Broken

Introduction

I am no longer the one to argue or debate about religion or spirituality. I will not go deep or become very theological. First of all, I am not an expert on theology, nor do I profess to know everything about the Scriptures. But what and who I am is a child of God, who loves God, and who attempts to live a godly life by seeking God's face through prayer, reading his word, fasting, and seeking the advice of other like-minded individuals. As I go through life, I must admit that I have failed, messed up, made mistakes, and missed the mark. The Lord knows that I have fallen down many times, but nevertheless I did get up. When I got up, I sometimes had to hold onto and steady my shaking knees, straighten my back, square my shoulders, lift my head, wipe the tears from my face, straighten my crown, and move forward. The following are some of my life experiences relating to what I believe to be broken within the church. In other words, I would like to point out some ungodly activities and behaviors which I have personally observed. Many of the following events and circumstances have increased and become more noticeable and unfortunately acceptable.

Looking Back

Before I go into details about being spiritually broken, please allow me a moment to walk down memory lane and reflect on my earlier memories of the church. As a young child, I remember going to church on a regular basis. My mother would often remind my siblings and me to take a handkerchief, a couple of pieces of peppermint, our Bible, and some money to place in the offering plate. I vividly remember the small storefront church; it was old yet sturdy. I remember the small choir marching in and waiting patiently to see my sister's smiling face. She was the last one to march in because she was often the tallest member of the choir. I remember the young organists playing out of key and missing notes because he was still taking organ lessons. Over the years he became quite proficient. I remember the ushers wearing bleach white gloves hovering over the offering tray as if it was gold. I vividly remember them taking up the offering. It was a bright silver plate-like tray with a red or sometimes green felt material that lined the bottom. I remember the secretary greeting visitors and sharing the minutes of the previous Sunday. I remember an A and B selection from the adult choir, followed by an A and B selection from the youth choir. I also remember the invitation for a visitor to give a response. I even remember the preacher starting his sermon in a low monotone and ending the sermon practically screaming and taking deep breaths between pauses. But my fondest memories were after service. Once the church service ended, the young children were sometimes allowed to purchase snacks at the nearby candy store. I often bought popcorn and or a sucker. Sometimes the church hosted a fundraiser and they sold chicken and fish dinners which they prepared in a medium-size kitchen, which was located in the back of the church. Once the cooking grease was hot, it did not take long for the chicken and fish aroma to engulf the small church and spill out into the neighborhood. The "mothers" of the church often made sure that everything ran smoothly. Their white aprons were securely tied around their waist as they placed chicken or fish into styrofoam containers. Each container had an entrée and four sides; greens, sweet potatoes, macaroni and cheese, and a corn muffin. A slice of pound cake was placed in a sandwich bag for dessert. I always thought those ladies were some of the best cooks in the world. I truly enjoyed the food and the fellowship. Those were the days!

My Mom

My mother was also an excellent cook. Her Sunday dinner specialties were southern-style homemade biscuits and gravy, made from scratch. She often cooked fried pork chops and firm oven-baked glazed sweet potatoes, topped with marshmallows. Mom would often toss raisins on top, which soaked up the sweet, succulent, sticky syrup of the sweet potatoes. She cooked her collard greens with fatback or salt pork. There was no lean meat in those greens; it wasn't until years later that mom discovered and started to cook with smoked turkey meat. She often made creamy hot macaroni and cheese baked with four different types of cheeses with extra butter. We washed it all down with either Coca-Cola, 7-Up, or Kool-Aid. For dessert, a deliciously rich and creamy homemade banana pudding or a fresh, sweet, golden brown, finger-licking good, cooked to perfection peach cobbler, with crispy buttery edges, topped with large sugar granules. As we all sat around the table, we always thanked God for his abundance. Those memories of my family sitting around the table sharing a meal are still so vividly etched into my memory. Now, mom didn't cook large meals every Sunday, but as far back as I can remember, Mrs. Fay did.

Mr. and Mrs. Fay

Mrs. Farrell was also an excellent cook. She and her family lived directly behind us. She would often invite my siblings and me over for Sunday's dinner. She had a large table, which took up most of the space in her dining room. The table was always full of food during Sunday's dinner. She was well known for her fluffy homemade buttery biscuits and golden brown southern- style cornbread, with crispy edges, which were perfect for dipping into her perfectly seasoned collard greens. She also had okra cooked to perfection in addition to her deep-fried crispy on the outside but yet juicy on the inside southern fried chicken. There was always some type of dessert, usually a large two or three-layered caramel or coconut cake. Whenever I asked to take an extra slice of cake home she would respond with a smile as she slightly tilted her head. She would then ball up her hand to make a fist and gently punch me on the shoulder. Without saying a word, she peered over the rim of her reading glasses and gestured toward the kitchen; that was her way of saying, "of course, go help yourself to another slice of cake."

I have so many fond memories of those Sunday dinners with my family and the Farrell family. Mr. and Mrs. Fay, which I had often called them for as long as I can remember. They were an older couple who were well known throughout the neighborhood. They were highly respected and were considered the patriarch and matriarch of the community. I remember both of them having such a warm, and pleasant smiles. They were genuinely good people. In addition to my mother and my grandmother, Mr. and Mrs. Ferrell had such a great impact on my Christian growth. They often shared their faith and their love for Christ Jesus; they always had a genuinely caring and loving heart. Later in life I met many parishioners who professed Christ but did not have that same loving spirit as Mr. and Mrs. Fay.

Unforgiveness

I recall a few years before my divorce; I believe it was in March 2007. It was at that time I learned that my husband was unfaithful to the marriage. I actually had known for years; just call it woman's intuition. But to hear him verbally admit his unfaithfulness created an unexpected wave of emotions to wash over me. My body went into a form of shock; it felt as if I was having a heart attack and a stroke at the same time. It was as if his admission had taken on physical form, and forcefully pushed me because I immediately stumbled off balance. I desperately reached for the nearest wall for support in an attempt to stop myself from falling. I was extremely hurt and angry. My anger turned into bitterness and eventually, the bitterness turned into unforgiveness. I knew the Bible said we should love and forgive one another, but this time I felt totally justified holding onto my hurt and anger. He had committed adultery, defiled the marriage bed, and broken our marriage covenant. He didn't deserve forgiveness. I had forgiven many people for many things, but this time I had convinced myself that I would never forgive him. And I felt justified in my belief. I had every right to hold onto this unforgiveness, so I convinced myself. But I was wrong; it's never right to hold onto unforgiveness. To hold and harbor unforgiveness toward someone can be extremely debilitating and crippling. It can also stifle your ability to grow spiritually. Eventually I forgave him, but I must say that it was not within my own strength. I prayed and asked God to show me how and help me to forgive and he did. With God's help, I was able to forgive my ex-husband and when I did, it was as if a weight was lifted off my shoulders. That same day I cried because I was so relieved and grateful that God was so patient with me. Now here I was, a

Christian, loving the Lord and going to church faithfully every Sunday. But yet, I was walking around on a daily basis hurt, angry, and harboring unforgiveness toward my then-husband. Again, I felt totally justified. But I was not justified; I was broken.

The Best Seat In The House

Have you ever heard a sleepy infant or a very active toddler cry or pout in the midst of a church service? Then to make matters worse the parent gently lifts the child up and constantly says excuse me as they step over other parishioners' feet to make their way to the end of the aisle. Then as quickly as possible they make their way toward the back of the church. In doing so, they firmly hold the whining or crying child while simultaneously trying to avoid the many condemning stares. I wanted to avoid that at all costs. When my grandchildren were infants and toddlers, I made it a point to sit on the last roll in the church. This allowed me easy access to the exit without disturbing the service. Although my grandchildren are no longer toddlers I continue to sit in the back row. Not knowing that individuals felt a certain way about sitting in the back of the church. Now let me preface the following statement before I move forward. I have been a member of four different churches throughout my lifetime, so the following scenario could have occurred at one or the other.

One particular Sunday I was sitting on the back row, speaking to another parishioner when an usher approached us. The usher asked the lady who was sitting next to me if she wanted to sit in a seat closer to the front row. The lady responded no and added that she was comfortable with her present seat. The usher appears shocked and taken aback that the lady did not want to move closer to the front of the church and she went on to insinuate and even blatantly state that there was more power in the front of the church. I guess she thought the Holy Spirit only moved amongst parishioners who sat within the first few pews of the church and God refused to move amongst individuals who sat in the back. One Sunday I invited a friend to church and as usual, I took a seat in the back row. Before I could get comfortable, he asked me if I normally sat there. I responded yes. He quickly expressed his discomfort and his displeasure with his seat. He went on to explain that he normally sat in the front of the church and was often acknowledged for his presence.

Now I get it; people often prefer to sit within a certain section of their church. Perhaps their friends and family members routinely gather within that area, or maybe over the years they just become comfortable sitting within a familiar area. I also understand that the front row is often reserved for guest speakers, ministers, and our senior citizens. I get it; I can understand that, but what I don't understand is the human proclivity to judge someone as less than, less important, or undeserving of a touch from the Holy Spirit because they sit near the back of the church. It's broken to believe that an individual sitting on the front row or near the front row is more important, righteous, wealthier, or deserving than those positioned near the back.

From Bibles To ~~Bibles To~~ Bluetooth

I miss those days when the pastor would give the morning scripture and immediately you heard the sound of hundreds of pages of the Bible turning as the congregations shuffled and thumbed through their Bibles to find the exact verse. I remember everyone at church having a Bible. I remember enjoying listening to the Bible pages turning in unison as the congregation searched for the morning scripture. Now in the twenty-first century, the turning of Bible pages has become almost non-existent. The Sunday service is now full of laptops, notebooks, nooks, and cell phones which many are equipped with and downloaded with Bible apps. Now when the pastor asks the congregation to turn to a certain scripture you can see all the electronic devices simultaneously light up. After reading the scripture, many of the electronic devices are switched from their Bible apps to Netflix, video games or some form of social media such as Facebook and Instagram. Some individuals may decide to check their emails or text. Now what I have observed a great deal of which was non-existent back in the day are children and teens sitting in church playing video games, watching movies, or texting on their electronic devices.

Spiritual and Spiteful

How can someone profess to be a Christian and love God but hate people? Have you ever met anyone who was self-righteous and sanctimonious on Sunday, then on Monday they were sarcastic and stuck up? Have you ever met an usher, a member of the choir, someone on the deacon board, or any member holding a position in the church whose personality did not resemble their position? For example, have you ever visited a church and the greeter did not greet or speak to you nor offer you a smile? I have; I once met an usher who was actually argumentative and very rude as she shut the church doors in my face. I gave her the benefit of the doubt; I thought she was having a bad day. But it turned out she was having a bad month, a handful of bad months to be exact. I also met a lady some years ago who was a Sunday school teacher. She taught young children many Bible stories about the love of Christ for over ten years. Her demeanor and behavior outside of the church were quite different from the behavior seen and exhibited within her church. I do believe we should make great attempts to walk in love, especially if we profess Jesus as our Lord and Savior. Now I do understand; I get it, none of us are perfect. We mess up, we miss the mark, and fall down. But when we ignore or don't address our mistakes, there lies the danger of becoming comfortable with bitterness, and strife, hatred and spiritually broken.

Reflection

The world in which we live is forever changing. This definitely applies to the church. I remember a time when the choir slowly marched into the sanctuary every Sunday. They would often take one step sway to the right, take another step, and sway to the left. They would continue this march in unison down the center aisle until they reached the choir stand, which was often positioned behind the podium. Currently today, I have seen choirs run, jump, and even breakdance onto the stage of the church. The church music and the message have also changed. Many years ago, the pastor's message was basic. On Easter, he would talk about the resurrection of Christ. During the Christmas season, he would talk about the birth of Christ. Throughout the rest of the year, the pastor would often preach about creation, the birth, death, and resurrection of Christ, the results of sin, and God's love and salvation. Today's Sunday sermon may consist of a variety of topics, for example, finances, entrepreneurship, relationships, marriage, homosexuality, and physical and mental health. There have been drastic changes within the church, and many of these changes are often applauded or appalled. As changes continue to occur within the church, it's imperative to be mindful that these changes remain rooted in godly principles.

Chapter 9
Broken Things

Introduction

Is it possible that you may have become comfortable with some broken items? Broken things may be found within your home, your place of employment, or wherever you find yourself spending a majority or a significant amount of your time. Things often in our possession become worn, damaged, and broken, causing the item not to function properly. The item becomes inoperable, no longer useful, enjoyable, and or possibly dangerous. Nevertheless, and for whatever reasons, many individuals refuse to throw out, discard or replace broken items. What are some broken things you have become comfortable with? Please let me share with you some broken items that I had become accustomed to and comfortable with. Is it possible that you may have similar broken items within your possession or within your immediate surroundings?

An Old Stove

During my childhood, I can recall several things in my home that were often in need of repair or needed to be replaced. My mother often held onto broken household items for months even for years. She was very resourceful and mechanically inclined. She was the one who would never shy away from work. I have vivid memories of my mother always working with her hands. She was always sewing, gardening, hammering, and eagerly attacking minor to major repairs within the house. She would prop up, wire up, pin up, nail up, stitch up, or tape up whatever needed repair. By doing so, it allowed the family to get more use out of the item. But what I know now that I didn't know then is that the longer my family was exposed to broken things throughout the house, the more we adapted to it and became comfortable with the broken items. For example, I recall when several of the knobs broke off of the stove. The stove initially became an eyesore. Everyone in the house took every opportunity to complain about the damaged stove. But over time the complaints stopped, and no one appeared to be bothered or even noticed the missing knobs. I vividly remember this one particular stove we had for several years. Over time and through wear and tear many parts of the stove became damaged or broken. Three out of four of the knobs were missing, and the oven door handle was extremely loose. The upper oven door handle was only attached with one small frill screw which allowed it to swing back and forth across the oven door each time someone opened it. The lower boiler door handle was bent. A screw was missing from the left side of the oven door, which caused the door to slightly separate, exposing the beige color, cotton fabric-like content within the two-ply oven door. This always gave the illusion that the oven door was slightly open. In addition, the oven's pilot light often malfunctioned. In order to heat the oven, my mother would use a long stick match, when one was available. But most of the time she would take a piece of newspaper, roll it up tightly, light one end of it with a match, and then place the flaming part of the newspaper into the back of the lower part of the oven in an attempt to ignite the pilot light. This caused the burners to emit blue, white and orange flames which would eventually heat the oven in order to bake. Attempting to turn your stove on as such can be extremely dangerous. It's a good practice to repair or replace broken or damaged items in an attempt to avoid injuries.

Stop On A Dime

A couple of years ago, while driving late at night, I hit a piece of metal lying in the middle of a dark road. I initially made great attempts to avoid hitting the object or slamming on my brakes because traffic was moving over sixty (60) miles an hour. So, I cautiously slowed down and maneuvered away from what looked like a scary, massive, and jagged piece of scrap metal, which possibly fell off from the back of someone's truck. In a matter of seconds, my car hit the large object. On impact, it literally sounded like an explosion, and momentarily my car shook violently. I immediately looked down onto the floor because it felt as if something had punctured its way through the floorboard of the car.

Once I was able to safely exit the expressway, it was only then that I discovered the extent of the damages. The large sharp piece of metal had punctured through the lower panel of the driver's side door and ricocheted up and broke the rearview mirror. The car was in the shop for almost two weeks. During that time, I rented a brand-new Toyota Corolla with less than 100 miles on it. It had that new car smell, fully loaded, comfortable, and had a smooth ride, and it stopped on a dime. Each day, for two weeks, I thought to myself, "I can get used to this." And that is exactly what I did; I quickly became comfortable with the smooth-riding experience of a new car. At that time, my car was eight-plus years old, with more than 100,000 miles on it. It did not run the same way as it did many years ago. When it came time to return the rental and pick my car up, it was both bitter and sweet. I had looked forward to getting back into the familiar surroundings of my car, but at the same time, I didn't want to leave the upgrades and the smooth ride of the loaner car. Once back in my car I immediately noticed that something was wrong with the breaks. I called the mechanic and voiced my concerns. They reassured me that absolutely no work was performed on or near the brakes. I quickly came to realize that I have been driving around with moderate to adequate breaks. And I had become comfortable doing so. I would have never discovered this if I had not had the opportunity to drive a brand-new car with excellent brakes.

A Clunker

"If I'm lucky, I can get five more years out of this car." Have you heard anyone say this, or have you yourself said this? I once knew a man who thought exactly like that. But he and I both knew that he would be lucky if he was only able to get five more miles out of the car. Let's refer to him as Jim. For several years he owned what we often refer to as a clunker. A clunker is an old worn-out vehicle, which is often an eyesore. While driving have you ever hit a pothole and thought nothing of it. At least not until maybe two days later when your muffler starts to drag. Well, that's exactly what happened to Jim. He drove over a large pothole which caused part of his muffler to disconnect and drag underneath the car. Somehow, he temporarily secured the muffler to the undercarriage of his car with what appeared to be a hanger or some type of wiring. This was initially supposed to be a temporary solution but turned into a permanent one. He would often say that one day he would properly have the muffler mounted. He also made several promises to repair his cracked windshield, fix his busted tail light, replace his almost bald tires, and bent antenna, and buff out the scratches on the driver-side door. In addition, there were rust spots, dents, and dings that were very noticeable throughout the car.

As he delayed, putting off repairing the car's many needed repairs, he slowly fell into a comfort zone of driving that vehicle for months. And I'm not pointing fingers because it's subtle and easy to do. Years ago, I found myself in a similar situation. Although my car did not require nearly as many repairs as Jim's car. Nevertheless, there were repairs that I often put off and ignored. I have to admit there was a time when I allowed my car to remain dirty for weeks, both inside and out. Nowadays, I'm much better, but it has truly been a process to keep my car clean. How many people do you know who have become comfortable riding around in a clunker or maybe a car full of trash?

Pete's Garage

I recall a time when a friend of mine purchased his first new home. The entire process was very exciting and rewarding. His diligence in saving, planning, and preparing had all paid off. It postured and positioned him to have his home built from the ground up. It was a major purchase and it was also a step toward independence of financial freedom. Approximately two years after Pete moved in, he noticed the overhead garage door which once made a very faint and unnoticeable sound when it lifted, now made a loud, annoying squeaky sound. He became concerned and immediately inspected the door. After several failed attempts to repair the door, he put his tools away and vowed to repair it on another day. Due to his hectic and demanding work schedule, repairing the garage door now had to wait. After several weeks had passed, the door had no longer become a priority. As several months went by the once irritating, squeaky sounds of the garage door no longer bothered him. The door remained broken for several months until someone accidentally ran their car into the back of his garage door and tore the overhead door completely off its hinges. He neither had the tools nor the know-how to replace his garage door. Due to safety reasons, he immediately called a professional to replace the door. Once the new door was installed, he was pleasantly pleased and ironically upset. He was pleased because the door went up and down smoothly with a faint sound. He was upset because he had allowed himself to become comfortable with the loud sounds of his broken garage door for almost a year.

Broken Food

Can you break food? Can food become broken? Yes, food can break, and yes you can become comfortable with broken food. First, let me explain how food can break and exactly what broken food is. Food becomes broken when it is spoiled, past its expiration date, moldy, tainted, or simply unfit to eat. By some means or through a process, food becomes inedible. For example; dairy, meats, fruits and vegetables may not be stored properly, which can cause breakdown, contamination and spoilage of food. Let me share with you how I became comfortable eating broken food. Now I will have to go back many years. As a young child, I can remember eating a variety of broken foods and I had become comfortable doing so. I had observed my family members consume these broken foods as well. Let me give some examples. Peanut butter and jelly sandwich and a cold glass of milk were one of my favorite meals. My mother attempted to always keep a large jar of peanut butter and jelly in the house. But on several occasions mold would grow on top of the jelly. The first time I saw it, it looked as if someone had placed a gray cotton ball in the jelly jar. When I discovered that it was mold, I became nauseated, my stomach felt queasy and I literally wanted to throw up. On another occasion when I discovered mold in the jelly, I attempted to throw it into the garbage, but my mother intervened. She took the jar and scooped out the mole and placed the jar back into the refrigerator. So, whenever I saw mold within the jelly, like my mother I spooned it out before making myself a sandwich. The same was true for a slice of bread; if there was a small amount of mold on the corner of the bread it was cut off before being eaten. It wasn't until years later that I discovered that simply cutting off or spooning out mold does not make the food edible. Although you may remove the visible part of the mold, there are still mold spores that still may not be seen within the food.

In the middle of the stove, my mother had a tin can that consisted of what my siblings and I referred to as her special sauce. It was a mixture of leftover grease and drippings after she fried or baked chicken, pork, or beef. This special sauce was used to refry other meats, bake cornbread, and season beans, greens, and other vegetables. I must admit mom's food was delicious, but now looking back, it may not have always been healthy for us to consume. On occasions I had seen mold grow on top of her special sauce. My mother didn't realize that just by spooning the mold out of her special sauce and the jelly or cutting the mold off of a slice of bread made the food safe to eat. From moldy jelly, expired meat, overly bruised fruits, and spoiled vegetables are all broken foods. Broken food has the potential to cause nausea, and digestive problems, which can also lead to severe health issues. Thinking back, as a child I had eaten many broken foods. Fast-forward to the present day; I'm happy to admit that I no longer consume broken food. Is it possible that you once consumed unhealthy food when you were a child? Is it possible that you have currently become comfortable eating broken food? Now I need you to think back, did your mother or grandmother ever have a grease can in the middle of their stove? Do you have a tin can or a glass jar positioned on top of your stove which contains your special sauce? Is there actually one in your kitchen today?

Bent, Busted, But Not Disgusted

How many things in your home that are broken and busted, but you're still not disgusted or fed up with it? Have you fallen into a habit of constantly putting off needed repairs? This often creates opportunities for individuals to become comfortable with broken things. Let me share with you some broken things that I grew up with. My mom always liked and enjoyed a large dining room table. I remember this one table which I particularly liked was my mother's favorite piece of furniture. It was a large heavy dark brown wood table with very intricate carvings of leaves on both the edge and the legs of the table. Each leg of the table rested on a ball-like wheel, which allowed the table to be easily moved. Unfortunately, one of the wheels broke and my mother placed a thick telephone book underneath the table leg, which surprisingly fit perfectly. My dad had promised my mom to repair the leg of the table as soon as he had the time. Least to say, the table remained broken for several months.

Unlike many years ago, today the average household has a television in each room. I grew up with one television in the entire house. It was a large, bulky floor model that rested on four legs. Over time one of the knobs broke off, revealing a protruding, one-inch piece of metal. We often used a pair of pliers to grip the piece of metal and turn it, which allowed us to change the channel. For convenience we would often place the pliers on top of the television. The pliers remained there for several months. I grew up with several broken items in my home which seemed to take forever to be repaired or replaced. When you continuously have been exposed to broken items as a child, we tend to remain comfortable with those identical broken items within our adult life. At least that was true for me. Is it possible that you have become comfortable with similar broken items from your childhood?

Junk Drawer

Many of us would be surprised at how many broken things we have around the house. Several of us even have a special place for our broken items. Usually there is some location in the house reserved especially for these items. This special place is often referred to as a junk drawer. Some broken items you may find in a junk drawer are batteries that no longer hold a charge, sunglasses with one missing lens, pencils that need sharpening, expired coupons, expired small packages of ketchup and soy sauce. Broken items unable to fit in a drawer are often stored in the garage, the attic, or maybe the crawl space within the basement. If not mindful, you can quickly accumulate several broken, useless, and unnecessary items. This can lead to an ever-growing concern, one of hoarding.

Reflection

Take a moment, and think about the many things you have promised yourself to fix or repair. What are they? What are some of the things you have been putting off? Is it possible that you have been procrastinating, delaying repairs on some of the following items: changing the oil in your car, sewing that button onto your coat, replacing the batteries in the smoke detector, replacing those two blown-out light bulbs in your bathroom vanity mirror, replacing the refrigerator's water filter, changing the ink cartridge in your printer, tightening that one loose knob on the top dresser drawer, or replacing the furnace filter? Are any of these items on your to-do list? When we put off or neglect to promptly repair small odd jobs or broken items, it usually creates bigger problems. In closing, I suggest that you promptly attempt to repair, replace, or remove the broken items from your home. In doing so, it helps to eliminate the temptation to become comfortable with broken things.

Chapter 10

Brokenness Identified

Introduction

Were you able to identify with any of the many scenarios within the previous chapters? Did any of the stories sound familiar? Were there any ah-ha moments? Were you able to identify broken areas in your life? Were you able to identify lack, sickness, obesity, or possibly ignorance, or abuse? You may or may not have; if not, that's understandable. I definitely can relate. For several years, I was unaware of many broken areas in my life. It was a failed marriage, and a divorce, which eventually highlighted and led to the exposure to toxic environments, people, thoughts, and other crippling and debilitating situations and circumstances. Oftentimes we don't know we are broken; we're unaware because we often create and reside within comfort zones of Inadequacies. A mentor once told me, "You don't know what you don't know." Is it possible that you're not further along in life, more successful, more prosperous, healthy, or more informed because you just don't know it? You may ask, how can I repair the brokenness if I don't know I'm broken? How can I heal if I don't know if I'm sick? How can I become rich if I don't know if I'm poor? How can I have a loving, caring relationship, if I have become comfortable with abuse and neglect? How can I conquer the self-defeating mindset if I believe I am not worthy or deserving? There is an old cliché that states, "if it's not broke, don't fix it." which basically means leave well enough alone. But what if something is broken? What if you're broken and you don't know that you need to fix it? Then there you will remain in a state of brokenness, possibly weak, sick, in debt and in poor relationships. And that's unfortunate, especially when compared to a more fulfilled life. Please be mindful that you cannot fix nor repair the broken areas until you're able to first identify the problem. Once the problem is identified, your opportunities to improve will increase.

The 5W's of Brokenness

In order to identify brokenness, I believe it would be helpful to first discuss the basic 5 W's as it relates to brokenness. Let me briefly give an overall view of the 5 W 's of the perspective "when broken feels right." The following is a brief description of who, what, when, why, where, and the how of brokenness.

Who

Who can break? Anyone can break, rich or poor, young or old. We all have the potential to break, that includes everyone from the womb to the tomb.

What

What is this concept of "When broken feels right?" It's an interesting perspective. It's a conscious or unconscious act of accepting lack, less, loneliness, lies, and other negative circumstances and or accepting and associating with negative, or non-supportive individuals.

When

When can an individual break? We can break from one extreme to another. An individual can break within any stage of their life. They can break within stages of depression, disappointment, and devastation. We can also break at stages of success, increase, and prosperity. We often tend to break within our childhood. Research shows that children are like sponges. When children are shown love and respect, or neglect, and abuse, they are more prone and more likely to repeat identical behavior.

Where

Where do we break? We can break in different areas of our life. Within the book, I focus on the following five areas in which we tend to break: spiritually, mentally, physical, financial, and relational.

Why

Why do we break? We often break because of the amount of time we invest in negative situations, circumstances, and or the amount of time we invest in negative or non-supportive individuals.

How

How do we repair the brokenness? That's your million-dollar question, and I have a million-dollar answer. In order to repair what is broken, there are several innovative techniques, and steps, which I shared in the following chapters. The first step is to recognize and identify what's broken

Shaken

I have come to shake you in hopes of awakening you to the possibility that you may be broken, not living to your fullest, possibly not experiencing greater things in your life. Some individuals live their whole life and are never aware that they are not living their best life. Then there are others who for whatever reason just come to the realization that something is wrong, something doesn't feel right. Maybe they feel as if something is missing in their life. The following parable is an example of such an individual.

There is a well-known biblical parable that speaks about a son who asked his father for his inheritance. The young man took his Inheritance and went out into the world, wasted all his money, and eventually ended up living in a pigpen. He ate what the pigs ate and slept where the pigs slept. His desperation led him to live and act like a pig for a duration of time. The Bible goes on to explain that one day the young man just came to himself. He decided to leave the pigpen and return to his father's house, a place of comfort and plenty. Is there a place you can go back to and start over again? Is there a place where you can go back to refresh and renew? Can you go back to your father's house or your mother's house? Is it possible to go back to at least a thought, a memory of when you once told yourself that you were going to do something different, something great with your life? Maybe you can't think that far back, or maybe you're still asleep, unaware that you have settled for less.

If that's the case, then I have come to shake you, awaken you to the fact that you may possibly have become comfortable and unaware of some broken areas in your life. If so, then consider this your wake-up call. You may not be in a pigpen surrounded by mud. But could it be possible that you are poor, mistreated, ignorant, and or sick and not know it? Is it possible that you have unconsciously settled and become comfortable with less? Is it possible that you have become comfortable living a life of mediocrity, barely getting by, being inadequate and even worse, not knowing it? Well, I have come to shake you from your daydreams, a nap, a deep sleep, or possibly a canna tonic state. Is it possible that many of us have fallen asleep and become comfortable with sickness, lies, poverty, mistreatment, abuse, and their likes thereof? I lived a great deal of my life as such. It was a failed marriage and eventually a divorce that had shaken me to my core, but it had also awakened and enlightened me to another level of thought, which transformed my life. My ex-husband walked out on me; in addition to the divorce process, both had violently shaken and pushed me out of my comfort zone. It was at that time, I started to take a closer look at the different areas in my life, which also led to a closer observation of my comfort zones.

Comfort Zone

A comfort zone is a physical or psychological construct wherein Individuals are often able to reside in peaceful and stress-free environments. A comfort zone is basically a place, an activity, behavior, or even a mindset that creates tranquility, harmony, and peace. It's a place of familiarity, where you're able to relax and enjoy your life while avoiding stressful and challenging circumstances. Although comfort zones can be a very tranquil and peaceful place, nevertheless it can cause individuals to become lax and unmotivated. Oftentimes people will not step out of their comfort zones because of fear. We are often fearful of failing or fearful of what other people may think, and speak. Fear was the number one reason why I adamantly refused to step out of my comfort zone. Refusal to step out of our comfort zones can stagnate, delay and or even prevent growth and advancement.

Stepping out of your comfort zone, if only momentarily, can expose, and highlight not only broken areas but can also create opportunities to repair them. And that in itself would be worth the effort. Stepping out of one's comfort zone will often take strength and courage. With that being said, I want to encourage you to be bold and find the strength to step out. Even if you come out stumbling, trembling, or maybe crying, just take that first step forward. I do understand that it can be extremely fearful, but I want to encourage you to at least make an attempt. No matter how small the attempt, just do something different. Do whatever you can to move out of your comfort zone. It can initially be something as simple as dining at a new restaurant, listening to a different radio station, or even getting out of your bed on the opposite side in the morning. Although it may seem very minuscule and insignificant, that small decision can lead to making greater ones. Simply doing something out of the norm can possibly expose broken areas in your life.

Stages of Brokenness

The ability to identify brokenness can vary from person to person. Some individuals can readily identify when things are not quite right in their life. It may take others a long time to recognize broken areas; then there are others who live their entire life and may never discover it. It wasn't until shortly after my divorce, that I discovered four levels of brokenness. Within each level I was able to identify some similarities and differences. This discovery provided a guideline and a place to begin to repair. Following are descriptions and examples of the four types of levels of brokenness: types O, C, E and D.

Type O

Brief description:

Type O brokenness can best be described as obviously oblivious.

Explanation:

Type O brokenness usually occurs when someone is clueless and unaware of their present state of lack, sickness, ignorance and other deficiencies. This often occurs due to the lack of increase and the lack of exposure to the finer things in life. It occurs when an individual becomes comfortable and relaxed within deficits.

Degree of difficulty to repair:

Type O brokenness is the most difficult to repair because it's the most difficult to identify. Some individuals don't know that they're not living their best life. You basically don't know what you don't know.

Example:

The following is an example of an O-type broken individual. Sometimes individuals live in poverty so long that they consciously accept it as a way of life. Have you ever heard someone say, "I was so broke that I didn't know I was broke?" Could that be you? At one point in my life, that was me. I had fallen into a comfort zone of lack. I was taking night classes and working a minimum-wage job. It was a time when I was single with two very young children. Money was scarce and I was constantly trying to work within a meager budget. At that time, I did not own a car; I relied on public transportation. I also relied on public welfare to help assist with daily needs; that was a very rough time in my life. But what I didn't know was that I had fallen into a comfort zone of lack and dependency.

I had begun to accept a defeated lifestyle of just getting by. I accepted my current living situation and my circumstances as if that was how things would always be. I unconsciously developed a defeated mindset. I began to think that I would always be on a fixed income, receiving a basic minimum-wage, living within a small one-bedroom apartment, and raising my children in a neighborhood of like-minded individuals. I thought that would be my lot in life. I did not know nor imagine the possibility of having a beautiful home built from the ground up. I was obviously oblivious to the fact that I could live within a more beautiful, and safer neighborhood and community. It wasn't until many years later that I came to realize that my immediate surroundings had an effect on my desires. In other words, one's constant exposure greatly influences an individual's preference. Initially, not realizing it, I had been exposed and had become comfortable with less. I eventually became complacent and unmotivated to seek out the greater or the finer things of life. Let me end this section with one of my favorite mantras: "exposure equals preference." This mantra is a constant reminder to remain cognizant of my environment and the people within it. I actually have this posted in my home, which creates a daily reminder.

Type C

Brief description:

Type C brokenness can basically be described as comfort in chaos and criticism.

Explanation:

Type C brokenness usually occurs when an individual routinely positions and/or surrounds themselves with argumentative, contentious, and or quarrelsome individuals. This will often Increase one's desire or the need to participate or initiate arguments, heated debates, scuffles or possibly physical fights. Sometimes, but not always, there is some degree of substance abuse involved, which will initiate or perpetuate the dissension. It's common for someone to surround themselves with an environment of chaos and conflicts. They appear comfortable surrounded by people who are argumentative and combative. They themselves may exhibit similar or identical characteristics and behaviors. These individuals are often identified as bullies, troublemakers, or haters. It's those individuals who initiate, encourage, and maintain discord.

Degree of difficulty to repair:

Due to the possible involvement and the use of substance abuse, the degree of difficulty to repair can vary. For me personally, my degree of difficulty to repair in type C brokenness was mild to moderate. Over the years I have made great attempts to avoid, lessen or eliminate my exposure to a negative environment and negative individuals.

Example:

I can very much relate to type C brokenness. I remained on this level of brokenness for many years. I developed and grew within type C brokenness mainly because of my ex-husband's infidelity, lack of empathy, and verbal and physical abuse. Those factors were often the catalyst that sparked strong disagreements, which frequently led to yelling matches. We often argued which would sometimes lead to physical altercations. I remember my mom used to often say, "It takes two to argue." She was basically trying to encourage me to remain quiet when he started to argue. I must admit at times I did make great efforts to ignore him, but most of the time I strongly felt a need to respond. My decision to respond often exacerbated the conflicts. The lease to say, those toxic conversations were often the catalyst that propelled me into an even more debilitating comfort zone, one of a toxic marriage. Unfortunately, there I remained for many years, comfortable in chaos.

Type E

Brief description:

Type E brokenness can best be described as excessive excuses.

Explanation:

This is the process by which individuals continually attempt to justify their poverty, sickness, ignorance, or negative circumstances. They often point fingers and blame something or someone for their inability to prosper and progress. The Individual constantly makes countless excuses as to why they can't succeed or get ahead. They refuse to take any ownership or accept blame for their misfortune,

Degree of difficulty to repair:

Type E brokenness can be extremely difficult to repair because of the individual's constant refusal to accept possible fault or blame in their misfortune. The individual will often make great attempts to justify their failures by making endless excuses or placing blame, even when they are at fault. Until the individual is able to own up to their responsibilities and take ownership of direct failures in their life, then they will continue to place blame and make excessive excuses.

Example:

Let's see, where can I start? First, let me give you some examples of what someone may commonly say who is possibly a type E broken individual:

* "I can't lose the weight because I just can't find the time to work out."

*" I can't go back to school, I'm too old."

* "He is a good man and he only hits me when he is drunk."

* "I can never get out of debt because prices are too high."

* "I can't get a job because of the white man; he is always trying to keep me down."

* "As a woman, I can't get that position, because they only hire men for upper management."

* "I can only make a certain amount of money because of the glass ceiling."

* "I'm divorced, I'm a single parent, I'm limited."

* "I'm too tall, I'm too short, I'm too fat, I'm too thin."

Excuses can go on as such. Do you often find yourself making excessive excuses for yourself and others? Do you constantly make excuses or try to explain your inabilities or lack of success? I know a young lady who once was in an abusive relationship, and continuously made excuses for her abusive boyfriend. She frequently shared with me that his abusive behavior was not his fault. She would often tell me that he didn't mean to hurt her and that he only hit her when he was drunk or had a bad day at work. She would also add that his job was very stressful. There were many times that she felt that it was her fault that he was abusive. There were times when he would hit her because she didn't clean up or have his dinner ready and warm when he came home. She was so badly broken. She remained in that abusive relationship for over seven years. I strongly believe that that abusive relationship lasted so long because she refused to face reality as she continued to make excuses for his behavior.

Now let me share with you some of my own personal excuses that I once told myself and others. Before going back to school and obtaining my bachelor's degree, I recall making several excuses. I used to tell myself that I was too old, tuition was too expensive, I was not computer savvy, there will be too much traffic, parking will be difficult, it would be too much work and it will be too hard. My list of excuses went on and on. Although many of my excuses not to go back to school were true, nevertheless I had to make a decision to not to allow excuses to prevent me from taking control of my life. I not only made excuses for myself, but I also made excuses for others. I recall I would constantly make excuses for my ex-husbands' adulterous behavior. I told myself, "He is going through a midlife crisis; it's just a stage." "All men cheat, and at least he's going for counseling." Those were just a few of the things I often told myself. I discovered that when you constantly make excuses for poor and toxic behavior it can delay or even destroy your goals and dreams. It wasn't until several years later that I had reached a place where I was able to start to make a decision to let go of people, relationships, conversation, train of thought, habits, and any and everything that was a threat to my peace, health, and wealth.

Type D

Brief description:

Type D brokenness can basically be described as delayed dreams.

Explanation:

People will routinely postpone or put off taking action to correct and or improve their behavior and circumstances. Within type D brokenness, there is a need, a desire to change, but nevertheless, you don't take the initiative to improve. Individuals will often hesitate to take action. They constantly put things off for a later day. They tell themselves, "I will do it next week, maybe in the fall, or after my birthday, next year for sure, or I might just wait till the kids are grown." Unfortunately, what often occurs is that they become comfortable with always wanting, or desiring to do something. Although they have good intentions to improve their life, they put off taking the necessary steps to reach their goals. It's the sudden development of an urgency or becoming eager to change. It's a strong feeling to improve in one or more areas of your life, coupled with procrastination. They basically become comfortable putting things on hold. Unfortunately, type D individuals often miss several opportunities, and over time it affects their drive and will deplete their motivation.

Degree of difficulty to repair:

The degree of difficulty to repair can vary. Within type D brokenness, I personally experienced mild to moderate degrees of difficulty to change. I found it more difficult to change in some areas in comparison to others. For example; in the area of my health, I found it easier not to procrastinate. I regularly took steps to improve my well-being. Simply because of the sheer fact that I did not like to feel weak, depleted, or in pain. Now in the area of relationships, it was quite different. I would often procrastinate in addressing issues or initiating needed conversations with individuals which possibly could have improved the relationship.

Example

Have you ever told yourself that you were going to get out of debt, lose weight, change jobs and work on improving your relationships? I must admit that I had promised to do all of those things plus more. After several promises, small attempts, and good intentions, I found myself with very little or no progress. I recall several years ago that I had put on an extra unwanted 30 pounds. It was at that time that I immediately decided to eliminate the extra pounds. If you noticed I said I had decided to lose weight. I had all good intentions and I thought a great deal about it. I even mentally formulated a plan. But what I failed to do was to act on it. Unsurprisingly, I found myself at the end of several months and still overweight even after a year. Although I had honestly planned to lose the extra pounds, it did not occur because of my procrastination. I lacked the initiative to act. It wasn't until I began to experience pain and sickness in my body that I became more than motivated to act. I was extremely inspired to lose the extra pounds and improve my health. Have you ever been excited and enthusiastic about doing something? For example, have you ever wanted to buy a house, buy a new car, start a business or go back to school? But unfortunately, as the years pass you find yourself still renting, driving the same car, still have not enrolled in the class, and you still have not started that business or even written out a business plan.

Comparison

I would like to briefly recap, summarize and compare the four types of brokenness which I believe would give greater insight and possibly assist in identifying possible broken areas in your life.

Type O (obviously oblivious) - these individuals are totally unaware of being broken. They have no idea that they're not living their best life, nor are they aware of possible increases. Due to a lack of awareness, individuals become comfortable with less.

Type C (comfortable in chaos) - unlike type O, type C individuals are aware of less, lack and opportunities to obtain more. But yet still, they find it difficult to pursue greater things because they are often distracted and or preoccupied with contention and discord.

Type E (excessive excuses) - type E broken individuals are unlike and often considered to be the opposite of type C broken individuals. Type C broken individuals often are combative, but nevertheless, they make no excuses for their negative behavior. Nor do they make excuses for living with lack. On the other hand, a type E broken individual constantly makes excuses for living with lack. In addition, they blame someone or something for their inability to prosper.

Type D (delayed dreams) - Type D broken individuals are somewhat similar in comparison to the type E broken individuals. Both types D and E are consciously aware of possible increases and success. Type E individuals might even make an attempt at success. But if they fail, they immediately make excuses as to why and possibly may not make further attempts. Type D individuals have good intentions, but they seldom act on them. They often fall into a comfort zone of "always going to do something" but never getting around to doing it. It's that individual who is always promising themselves that they will start tomorrow. But then the next day is today, and tomorrow never comes.

Living My Best Life

Before we move onto the reflection part of this chapter, I would like to share with you what a friend of mine described as an epiphany. As I listened to him, I thought to myself that I must include his story in my book. I had to share it because it's an excellent example of discovering and identifying one's brokenness. He went on to explain how he came into sudden insight and revelation of a new way to live. He described a time when he felt as if he was suddenly shaken, awakened out of what appeared to be a daydream, a haze, or a mist of a life that had become his reality. Let's give this gentleman a name; of course, it's not his real name, but let's call him Paul. Paul explained to me that prior to his epiphany, he thought he was living his best life. He often shared and repeated this to several of his family members and friends as well. In spite of his thoughts of living his best life, he discovered that he had actually lived a large part of his life broken. At that time, Paul was almost 52 years of age, single, and living in a modest one-bedroom apartment. He had paid his car off, and considering that it now had a few miles, the car still ran very well. He was employed and had a good job, which he worked at for several years. He made enough money to pay his rent, utilities, and other monthly obligations. Occasionally, he could take a vacation or plan a weekend getaway about once a year. After several failed attempts, he was finally able to accumulate some savings. He was now doing it; he was living his best life, although he thought.

One day he realized that he was not living his best life; he realized that he could have been living a better life. He realized he hadn't followed through on his plans. Paul put off doing things he had promised to do months, even years ago. He had not made follow-up calls, go to the gym, lost weight, saved money, started his business, bought a new car, or purchased a home. He had fallen into a comfort zone of putting things off. He fell into a mindset of procrastination, which led him into a comfort zone of settling and accepting less. He did not realize this. It wasn't until he ran into an old friend, who happened to be more than ten years younger than him. Although Paul's friend made less money, he had acquired a home and two cars, managed to create and maintain savings, and he was in the process of starting a small business. As Paul and his friend reminisced and caught up, Paul couldn't help but think about all the things he had not accomplished. It was as if his friend had thrown a mirror up in his face, which revealed a life reflection of who Paul had once aspired to be. As the man continued to share his accomplishments, Paul couldn't help but feel jealousy, envy, and regret. Prior to meeting this man, Paul was content with his life. He was enlightened that day and came to realize that he was nowhere near living his best life. Paul was actually living only a fraction of what his life could truly be.

Reflection

After enduring a breakdown in my marriage and eventually divorced, I found myself pushed out of several of my comfort zones. It was here on the outside of my comfort zone that I discovered that I had only lived within fragments, only broken pieces of a marriage. Unfortunately, it took me several years to identify many of my broken areas. Individuals can live their entire lives broken and not know it. If I had stayed in that toxic marriage, I truly don't believe that I would have been able to identify many broken areas in my life. I hope this chapter becomes a baseline, a starting point, or even a catalyst to the discovery of your broken areas. Once you identify the brokenness, you can begin to implement strategies to repair it. The following chapters offer several ideas and techniques which were implemented in my personal life, which have willed positive results.

Chapter 11

Home In, Hatchet; Bury It, Habits

Introduction

I would like to reiterate how important it is to first identify your brokenness. This first step has the potential to set you on a path, a journey to your increase. Identification is actually the initial step that can lead to abundance, growth, strength, and repair. Once you identify what's broken in your life, that's a major step. After reading the previous chapters, what was the one thing that you identified with? What was it that you were able to relate to? Was it negative thoughts, an abusive relationship, an unhealthy lifestyle, or possibly a toxic friendship? Let me share with you some of the things that I had unconsciously become comfortable with: obesity, lack, less, abuse, sickness, and the list went on. I like to suggest several steps, strategies, and techniques which I implemented in my personal life on a daily basis. Over time I began to observe positive results. I became greatly encouraged and motivated. I was extremely excited about the changes taking place in my life.

The following are a list of ideas and a course of action that helped me take my life to another level of increase, passion and enthusiasm. In order to explain the strategies, I implemented into my life many years ago can best be described with an acronym. It so happened that I was able to come up with an acronym for the word help. I took each letter within the word "help" to explain each technique. Each letter in the word help represents strategies to repair. The following are twelve descriptive techniques, which include three steps, descriptive of each letter within the word help; such as H: home in, hatchet, habits, E: exercise, educate, exposure, L: live, leave, level up, P: plan, push, and prayer. As I began to implement each of the 12 steps, I realized some were more difficult to accomplish than

MILDRED "MICKEY" GIVENS

others. Working through each area was truly a challenge and a process. A process that was much needed and which proved to be very beneficial, and even life-saving. As we move forward throughout the next four chapters, I would like to share with you my experiences, my triumphs, and my struggles within each of the twelve categories. I have broken each one down into four practical parts to help give greater clarity in hopes of yielding greater results. The four areas within each technique are as follows: description, roadblock, how-to, and summary. Within each description section, I briefly explained the technique. Each roadblock section describes possible challenges and hurdles you may face. Each "how-to" section offers suggestions as to how to avoid, and/or overcome roadblocks, and obstacles. Each section titled summary offers an overview, encouragement, and my final thoughts pertaining to each individual technique.

Home In - Description

The first strategy I would like to address is entitled "home in." This is one of the first steps that I initially implemented once I identified the broken areas in my life. "Home In" is the process by which an individual develops laser beam focus. It's the capability of strategically moving toward one's target or goals with the ability to ignore neither to allow distractions to delay or prevent repair and/or corrections. In other words, "home in" is descriptive of maintaining one's focus.

The term "home in" can also be descriptive of how a missile approaches its target. For example, some fighter pilots are known to fly planes that are equipped with heat-seeking missiles. These planes have the capability of hitting their target even though it may be a long distance away and even out of the pilot's view. This also holds true for you and I. We have the ability to develop similar attributes to that of an infrared missile. Just like that missile, you can also target and launch out toward your desired goals, even though they may appear far away, out of reach, and unobtainable.

Home In - Roadblocks

I must admit that it was often challenging to maintain my focus. Circumstances and certain individuals became great distractions, which created stumbling blocks in my roadway of better, and my pathway of repair. My failed marriage led to a bitter divorce, which was a monumental distraction. During the first stages of my divorce, I initially found it extremely difficult to focus. The majority of the time, I was focused on the divorce proceedings. My days were mostly consumed with meetings and telephone calls. I had the arduous task of gathering financial statements as I attempted to break down the past 22 years of marriage into a spreadsheet. My once dreams and goals had taken a backseat to reading, analyzing, and organizing mounds of legal papers, attending court appointments, and endless meetings with realtors, lawyers, and paralegals. And oftentimes feeling alone throughout the process and working through hurtful and draining emotions. Overall, it was extremely taxing and consumed a great deal of my time and energy. What is it that zaps your energy and possibly takes up most of your day? What or who is it that has distracted you? Unlike myself, it may not be a divorce; but could it be a toxic relationship, an unfulfilled career, wayward children, or failing health? What is the one thing that gets in the way of your desires, your dreams, or your destiny?

What's the one thing, or possibly that one person that has created a roadblock, which has now allowed you to shift your focus.

Home In - How To

Although distractions can make it extremely difficult to maintain one's focus, nevertheless it's not impossible. The following is a list of behaviors and activities I implemented in my life in an attempt to maintain my focus. On a daily basis, I would often read and or listen to audiobooks that motivate, encourage and inspire me to stay on track. In addition, I also often wrote out a to-do list, which helped me stay focused on more pressing matters. This list was often compared to less important tasks which could be completed at a later date. This comparison allowed me to work on items that had time restrictions and fast-approaching due dates. By doing so, I was able to maintain my focus and complete tasks that took precedent. I discovered that the more I concentrated on and completed the task at hand, the less distracted I became.

I utilized my many post-it notes, which I positioned on my bathroom mirror, my nightstand, the refrigerator, my computer screen, and my car visor, and I affixed some on or near a few doors throughout my home. Each post-it note revealed an encouraging scripture or a motivating phrase. I could not go throughout my day without being encouraged by one of the small brightly colored post-it notes. I also utilized a vision board. In short, a vision board is a layout or a collage of pictures, words, and phrases that describes and hopefully motivates individuals to transform their life to reflect on the items on the board. Once you create a vision board, it's extremely important to place the board in a place where you can clearly and readily observe it. I have observed many family members and friends successfully implement similar techniques.

Natalie, my oldest daughter, has a large bathroom with a very large vanity mirror, which she often uses as a vision board. Each morning when she looks into her mirror, she is encouraged by two, or three handwritten notes, which she has taped within the right-hand corner of her bathroom mirror. Within the same corner, you will also find other positive quotes, which she has beautifully written directly onto her mirror with a bright red colored lipstick. Each morning when she glances into her mirror, she is encouraged by each quote. It helps her set the tone and focus for the day. My youngest daughter Delana and my granddaughter, Ciniyah have both created a digital vision board which they have downloaded and saved as their phone's screensaver. Each time they turn their phone on, they are motivated and encouraged to maintain their focus. They are constantly reminded of their dreams and goals.

I must admit that the post-it notes, the to-do list, and even the vision boards did not have a great impact on maintaining a positive focus until after I was first able to deal with and work through the hurt of the divorce. I joined a divorce support group and connected with some amazing instructors, counselors, and other individuals who were going through or had gone through a divorce. This small team of individuals offered lifesaving advice and counseling throughout an eight-week program. They offered and provided helpful resources, tools, and strategies on how to heal throughout the entire divorce process. It wasn't until after I had completed two sessions of the divorce support group that I felt as if I was able to focus on other things besides my divorce. It can be very difficult to focus when you are in distress. If you feel overwhelmed and are continuously feeling emotionally hurt, I suggest you seek help. Possibly seek professional counseling, ministerial support, a support group, or friends and family members who are understanding and supportive of what you are going through.

Home In - Summary

I recall a time when I was thirty pounds heavier, and all I could do was focus on the extra weight. My mirror and my scale were a constant reminder of the unwanted pounds. It was not until several years later that I was able to shift my focus from the extra pounds to my desired weight. I first stopped complaining about the extra pounds, and I stopped telling people that I was going to lose weight. I also implemented several strategies mentioned in this chapter, which wield tremendous results. I'm happy to say I lost thirty pounds. But in order for me to maintain the weight loss, it's pertinent that I maintain a daily focus. The following is an acronym I came up with for the word "focus"; Forcing Oneself to Concentrate Under Stress. I must admit that sometimes it would take all that was within me in order to focus. Distractions have the ability to detour and delay your dreams, but one's renewed focus can turn your life around. To repair what's broken, we must focus on the change we want to see in our lives.

We are currently living in an informational world. On a daily basis, we are exposed and inundated with so much information. It seems as if everyone wants your attention; they are trying to get your focus. In order to maintain one's focus, one might have to take extreme measures even if that includes turning off the television, the radio, and social media, if only momentarily, to regain focus. Currently, things around me do not resemble where I'm striving to be. My mirror doesn't always reflect how I desire to look. I'm not driving my dream car, nor do I live in my dream home. Are these some of your exact sentiments or concerns? If so, it can all change with a simple shift in your focus. In closing, whatever it is that you would like to focus on, first imagine it and then create a detailed picture in your mind. Next, I suggest you draw a picture of it or write a description of it on a piece of paper. Another suggestion would be to create a vision board. I also believe it's helpful to recite affirmations. In other words, speak out loud the things you hope to see transpire within your life. Lastly, intentionally act and move in the direction of your vision, and your goals. Purposeful movement often creates progress and results. Which often motivates you to maintain your focus.

Hatchet; Bury It - Description

Now, I know you're probably wondering how in the world a hatchet is going to help improve the broken areas of your life? Well, wait a minute, and let me explain. Have you ever heard the old cliché "bury the hatchet?" Have you ever wondered what it actually means? It's an old term derived from Native American culture. Hatchets were buried by the chiefs of tribes when they came to a peace agreement. Usually, the chief of each opposing tribe would bury a hatchet within the ground which symbolizes peace between two once warring tribes. By physically burying the hatchet, the two tribes agreed that fighting would cease, and they would live together in peace. In short, burying the hatchet meant to come to a mutual agreement and call a truce. To bury the hatchet can also be translated as the following: let bygones be bygones, forgive and forget, and turn the other cheek. These are well-known practical gestures that are extremely beneficial if practiced. By doing so it can save your relationships, your sanity, and even possibly your life.

Here within the content of this section of the book, a hatchet will represent anything that resembles or encourages dissension, strife, hatred, and such. Within this section, I would also like to strongly encourage you to bury your hatchet. In other words, don't allow mistreatment and negative emotions to deter you away from your life plans. A hatchet can vary from person to person. Your hatchet may represent negative emotions, thoughts, or actions toward someone. My hatchet was bitterness and anger toward certain people. I also had a tight grip on my hatchet of unforgiveness. It wasn't long before I discovered that holding onto unforgiveness, hurt, and other stressors have the ability to create stress within the body. And I cannot emphasize enough the fact that stress kills. I came to the conclusion that if I wanted to heal, and if I wanted to live a long healthy life, I had to bury my hatchet. With God's help I was able to relinquish and let go of bitterness, resentment, stress, and even unforgiveness.

Hatchet; Bury It - Roadblocks

Although practical and beneficial, it can be quite difficult to let bygones be bygones or turn the other cheek. I knew I needed to forgive and forget. I knew I initially should have forgiven him but I could not. My pride, anger, and frustration made it difficult to do so. I didn't want to let him off the hook. That would be too easy, and I felt extremely justified in not doing so. To be honest with you, initially, it was difficult to forgive him and let go of my bitterness toward him. I even told the Lord, "My husband cheated on me, he hurt me, he lied to me, but don't worry about it Lord, I got this."

Because of his infidelity, I strongly believed he did not deserve forgiveness, but I believed he deserved the cold shoulder and the silent treatment. He no longer deserves special treatment. He no longer deserved to be greeted at the door when he came home from work. He no longer deserved specially cooked dinners, a foot massage, a warm bed, or other marital-related bliss. I had made myself judge and jury. It was my way of receiving some small form of retribution, getting him back, and making him pay for what he did to me. I wanted him to feel sad because of how he made me feel, which was both physically and mentally drained. I thought I had the right to no longer be kind, loving, and respectful. I quickly discovered that holding back daily kind gestures was to no avail. Everything I did, didn't faze him or bother him in the least. On days that I did not cook, he went out and bought fast food. On the days I didn't speak to him, he ignored me and watched television or talked on his cell phone. When I showed no interest and made no advances to have sex, he seemed unbothered. None of the things I did seem to bother him in the least, but surprisingly it bothered me. His responses only added insult to injury. I became more frustrated, hurt, and stressed. Holding onto bitterness, anger, and even unforgiveness can create a large amount of tension and stress on the body. My stress levels had become overwhelming and even crippling. I became extremely distracted; I was unable to focus. It had become difficult to function and complete simple everyday tasks. I had to do something; I had to bury the hatchet.

Hatchet; Bury It - How To

As I sat on the couch and wiped the many tears from my face, I began to pray and desperately asked God to help me. I immediately heard a voice within me that stated "go get the book off the shelf." I paused, set up straight, and waited a few minutes before standing up and walking into a small reading room, where I had shelved approximately two hundred books and Periodicals. When I walked into the room there was one book that stood out and caught my attention. I pulled it off the shelf, opened it, and immediately noticed a Bible verse; If you don't forgive others, God will not forgive you." (Matthew 6:15). That day I asked God to help me forgive my ex-husband, and he did just that. Now it did not occur overnight, but with continual prayer and regular reading of scriptures I was eventually truly able to forgive him. The bitterness and strife that I was harboring began to dissipate. It literally felt as if a weight was lifted off my shoulders. It was then and only then that I was able to shift my focus from bitterness to one of peace and genuine love. Within that moment I so strongly felt the love and peace of God.

Daily prayer and scripture reading greatly assisted me in forgiving others. Once you bury your hatchet, I strongly suggest that you do not go dig it up again. Digging up one's hatchet occurs when you find yourself rehearsing, rehashing and reliving your past hurts. Sometime after my divorce, I found myself digging up my hatchet. I fell into a pity party, and momentarily I felt sorry for myself. I began to tell anyone who would listen how he mistreated me. Eventually, those conversations led to feelings of malice and increased ill thoughts toward him. I did not like the way it made me feel. One day in the middle of one of my pity parties, I stopped and verbally said out loud," I cannot do this." That day I made a conscious decision. I decided to stop talking about him and telling people how he mistreated me. I actually started to pray for him, and wish him well. Lastly, I stopped attending pity parties. This allowed me to start focusing on myself and my future.

Hatchet; Bury It - Summary

Today, Individuals are so transparent; they are so angry and frustrated. They are mad at the world, their spouse, and even mad at themselves. The idea of "burying the hatchet" was extremely instrumental in the repair of my broken life. My mother was also extremely helpful. She helped me bury many of my hatchets by way of her examples. My mother buried the hatchet like no other person I know. She was the best hatchet burier. I have never known her to harbor offense or hold grudges. She was a master at forgiving and forgetting. I recall as a young child, saying or doing something to upset my mother and later that day, I would go to her and apologize. Her response was often pleasant. Before I could finish my apology, she would lovingly glance at me, and in her soft monotone southern drawl she stated, "Girl, if you don't get on out of here, I done forgot all about it." This constant loving display of forgiveness motivated me to do the same. It wasn't until many years later that I was even able to attempt to mimic her ability to forgive quickly.

I asked her one day how she was able to quickly forgive and not harbor bitterness toward someone who had mistreated her. She went on to explain that people are often hurt, and they disguise it in the form of anger. She had a gift for distinguishing individuals' anger from their hurt. She further explained to me that individuals often want to be vindicated for the wrong they endured, even if it's in its simplest form of an apology. I have witnessed individuals make great attempts to obtain an apology from someone who has no intentions of giving one. If the apology is forced or demanded from someone, it will often be offered in pretense. Many years ago, I would often allow weeks, months, and even years to go by before I was able or even willing to offer an apology or forgive someone. Are you currently angry at someone and refusing to forgive them? Is it possible that you may be bitter, frustrated, or jealous? If so, harboring such negative emotions has the potential to create stress, and unchecked stress can have a detrimental effect on both one's mind and body. If stress is not addressed it can have devastating repercussions on you and inadvertently create stress on your loved one. Whatever your hatchet may be: hatred, envy, strife, or unforgiveness, if you don't find a way to bury it, it just might eventually bury you.

Habits - Description

Before you continue to move forward within this section, I suggest that you first take a moment to either write down or take a mental note of your daily routines. Many of us possess a daily routine of activities that we perform automatically and often unconsciously enough. Now think about or take a good look at your list and evaluate it. These daily routines have the potential to become lifelong habits. Habits are rituals and behaviors that are usually performed on a daily basis. They are often repeated without much thought. The following habits are repeated automatically, such as washing our face and brushing our teeth in the morning. Such simple routines can become involuntary, for example looking both ways before crossing the street. A behavior or a thought constantly repeated has the ability to form and create our habits. And these behaviors can be either productive or destructive, helpful or a hindrance. Exercising, and eating healthy foods, are often considered good habits. On the other hand, smoking, drinking, overeating, and many other routine negative behaviors are often considered bad habits.

There was a time in my life that I made choices to overpay and overspend, which led to an abundance of debt. I can recall a time when I constantly ate fatty and sugary foods, which led to overweight and ill health. As the years passed, it became very apparent that my poor habits had caused my debt to escalate and my health to decline. I knew it would be difficult, but nevertheless I decided to change my habits. I had made a decision to take a closer look at my habits, evaluate them, and adjust my behavior in an attempt to alter and create new and productive ones. I also knew it would not be a small feat.

Habits - Roadblock

I was more than ready and eager to start my new habits, but I quickly discovered that there were roadblocks to creating them. It was not as easy as I thought. Let me share some roadblocks as to why many individuals are unable to change their habits. I have some ideas; they don't want to, they don't know how to, laziness, procrastination, fear, familiarity, comfort zones, cognitive psychology, friends, and associates. Maybe some of these reasons prevented you from starting new habits. Have you ever tried to stop an old habit or start a new one, only to find it extremely difficult to do either? Well, you are not alone; many people have found this to be a very challenging deed. Have you ever wondered why? As I reminisce back on my past, I can immediately recall the top four obstacles which made it very difficult for me to change my habits.

My top four roadblocks were fear, procrastination, my associates, and the way my brain was wired. Amongst them all, I believe my biggest roadblock to change was fear. I was fearful that if I tried something different that it wouldn't work out. I was also fearful of other people's opinions of me. I used to wonder if I changed, would they still approve of me? I remember back in 2015 when I had an idea, a thought to go on Facebook and create short videos to motivate individuals. That was my first thought; my second thought was full of fear, what would people think, what would people say? Fear appeared to be forever at the forefront of my mind. That fear became the catalyst for my procrastination. Deep down inside I had a strong desire to do the videos, but I found myself dragging my feet when it came to actually creating, practicing, and posting the videos. I often told myself that I would do it next week or I convinced myself that I really didn't have the time. In addition to fear and procrastination, some of my friends were also a huge stumbling block when I attempted to create new habits. There were individuals who immediately encouraged and motivated me to do the videos, but on the other hand, there were others who constantly discouraged me. For a brief moment, I contemplated not posting on social media.

Lastly, I discovered that the way in which my brain was wired prevented me from starting new habits. University research shows that 40% of human behavior is derived from habit and not one's choice. Research has proven that it can be difficult to change one's habits because of the way our brains are wired. Some experts believe it has a great deal to do with cognitive psychology. Studies have shown that parts of our brain have the ability to reinforce our habits, which can make it difficult to alter our behavior. In short, when we develop a habit, our brains create new neurological pathways which allow us to easily continue that particular habit. Now the flip side of that coin is that when you no longer desire to continue the behavior, we often find it difficult to stop. The reason is that your neurological pathways make it easy for you to repeat old behaviors, which we often repeat unconsciously.

Habits - How To

There are three basic components to creating new habits; cues, behavior, and rewards. A cue is something, or possibly someone that triggers or stimulates one to act. The behavior is the act, the response to the cue. The reward is something you obtain after the desired behavior. Now let me bring this all together and give you an example. A friend of mine wanted to get into the habit of exercising early in the morning to lose weight. So, each morning she would get up early, go to the gym, work out, and return home to shower before she went off to work. The cue/triggers: The break of dawn or the first ray of sunlight coming through her bedroom window. Sometimes it will be the soft buzzing sound of her alarm clock. The behavior: jumping in her car and driving to the gym to work out. The reward: calories burned, a burst of energy and increased clarity of how to start her day. Starting a new habit can be difficult. When I initiate new habits, I consider the following four components: setting goals, accountability partner, affirmations, and self-discipline.

Goal Setting

After the birth of my youngest child, I noticed I had put on some extra unwanted pounds. I neither felt nor looked my best. Roughly within a ten-year period, I had gained sixty pounds. Gradually I adjusted the notches on my belt, bought larger size clothes, and avoided my scale. I lived my life like this for a while until one day I ran across a picture. Someone had taken a picture of my backside while walking past our Christmas tree. I laugh about it today, but as I stared at that picture I thought if I had on a pair of red pajamas that morning someone could have easily mistaken me for Santa Claus. It was that day that I decided to lose weight. I needed to increase my workout time and decrease the many calories I consumed, but how? I needed a plan, but first I needed to come up with some achievable goals. I first wrote my goal out on a piece of paper. My goal was simple; I wanted to lose ten pounds in one month. I also wrote out a schedule detailing the dates and times as to when I would work out. Lastly, I created a menu and a list of lean protein and healthy fruits and vegetables to routinely purchase. I focused on my goals daily. Over time not only did I lose the extra pounds, but I also developed lifelong healthy habits.

In addition to physical goals, I also developed new habits by setting financial goals. For example, many years ago I attended a seminar on how to create an emergency fund. I honestly didn't think it would work. Nevertheless, I gave it a try. I immediately wrote out the following steps as to how to create and adhere to a new budget; shop for groceries once a week, eliminate fast food, and pick up extra hours at work. These new habits helped create extra streams of income, which increased my savings, and in turn created an emergency fund, which was my initial goal. Mind you it took several months to build my emergency fund, but in the process of doing so, I was also building and maintaining new habits.

Accountability Partner

Once you target your goals and implement a plan to achieve them, then immediately connect with someone who can assist or even simply motivate you to reach your goals. A good accountability partner has the ability to encourage others to accomplish their goals. They should be honest, reliable, and not judgmental, which will allow you to freely share your ideas, progress, and or setbacks. They should also have the ability to check on you, to check on your progress and the lack thereof. If you're unable to get one person who possesses all these qualities, then it's ok to ask two or even three individuals to be your accountability partner. One may have the ability to be brutally honest and tell you when you're lacking or being lazy, and they do it with your best interest at heart. Another may possess the ability to encourage you in such a way that it sparks immediate enthusiasm and energy which motivates you to continue or restart your quest. Let your accountability partner know exactly what you need from them. You may need them to call, text, or even make house calls as you attempt to create your new habits. For whatever reason, if you're not able to delegate an accountability partner to encourage you, then encourage yourself! It's not only important to encourage yourself but to also reward yourself as well. When you reward yourself, it high-light your accomplishment which often motivate you to repeat the behavior.

Affirmations

Affirmations are positive words or phrases that individuals repeat in hopes that what they verbally speak out loud would manifest and become a reality in their life. Some commonly known affirmations which people often repeat: "I am healthy and I am wealthy." Some experts believe that spoken affirmations have the ability to affect the subconscious mind. Research shows that more than 50,000 different thoughts can cross your mind in one day which is comparable to 150 to 300 thoughts in one minute. Unfortunately, 80% of the time most of those thoughts are negative. But on a positive note, it's believed that you can reverse the negative thoughts to one of the positive thoughts by speaking positive affirmations. It's believed that daily repeated verbal affirmations have the ability to eventually affect and change one's behavior, which can lead to the development of new habits. And I for one also believe this to be true. For many years now, I have attempted to say positive affirmations on a daily basis. I often recite my affirmations first thing in the morning, oftentimes before I get out of bed. I have also been known to recite them in the shower, driving in the car, or just randomly throughout the day. As I speak my affirmations, I also creatively visualize them. It's through my creative visualization that I'm able to have a greater focus which motivates me to act. Continuous and repeated action has great potential to form new habits.

Self-Discipline

Reciting affirmations, connecting with an accountable partner, and setting goals will not have long-lasting effects if you are not self-disciplined. Self-discipline is basically the ability to discipline oneself. This often requires a great deal of willpower and fortitude. I remember growing up and telling my mom when I did not feel like doing something. She would often look at me and respond, "Your feelings have nothing to do with it." She emphasized that I needed to do what was required of me regardless of whether I felt like doing it or not. She basically tried to convey to me that regardless of my feelings, I needed to do what she asked me to do. I didn't know my mother was attempting to help me develop self-discipline skills at that time. I'm so grateful for my mother's life lessons. They taught me that self-discipline is the foundation on which to build long-lasting habits.

Habits - Summary

Forming new habits can vary from person to person. Some say it takes 21 days; others believe it takes more or less. Simply put, we develop new habits one decision at a time followed by a repeated behavior. I have witnessed individuals instantly develop new habits. For example, I have observed women who were heavy smokers instantly stop once they discovered that they were pregnant. I have also witnessed my mother instantly change one of her lifelong habits. Please let me briefly reminisce and share how she did it. For many years during the holidays, my family followed certain traditions. We usually met at my mother's or sister's house on Christmas Day. We ate, played games, and when it came time to open presents, mom usually sat near the corner of the couch as her children and grandchildren brought her gifts. One year, maybe a couple of weeks before Christmas, my mother announced that she was going out of town. She wanted to spend Christmas with her siblings who all lived in Nashville Tennessee. "Say it isn't so!" My siblings and I were all in disbelief. There was no way mom wouldn't be home for Christmas, so we all thought. My mother did go out of town that year and other years that followed. I initially asked my mother why? She stated that she wanted to do something different on Christmas. With that one single decision, she stepped out of her comfort zone and immediately created a new habit. Unbeknown to her, that one decision would affect generations to come. Although my mother did not spend every Christmas out of town, it did impact several family members. I noticed that in the years that followed, some other family members broke holiday traditions. Consider your habits because they can be very influential, even after death. Your habits have the ability to affect not only your immediate family but also several generations that will follow. Traditions are only habits, which are repeated in each generation.

Chapter 12

Exercise,

Educate,

Exposure

Exercise - Description

What is the mental image, or what picture pops into your head when someone brings up the topic of exercising? Do you immediately imagine your local gym full of individuals running on a treadmill, the elliptical, or people lifting heavy weights? Did you visualize a basketball, tennis court, a large football field, or other sporting events? Maybe you imagined an ice rink, a swimming pool, or possibly a nearby park with a walking path. Could it be that you pictured yourself gardening or house cleaning? Each of these activities is a form of physical activity which has the ability to elevate one's heart rate. Exercise is some form of physical activity including walking to increase mobility and stamina and running to increase cardiovascular health. Lifting weights is another form of exercise that builds muscles, in addition to yoga and stretching which often increase flexibility. Whatever your choice of physical activity, experts suggest that we participate in some form of exercise on a regular basis. Exercise has the ability to add to the quality and longevity of one's life. Research also shows that even the smallest daily recommended amount of exercise has so many benefits to both the body and the mind. Despite the fact that there are endless benefits to working out, many of us choose to live a sedentary lifestyle.

Initially, I never thought much about exercising or nutrition until my health was compromised. I remember a time in my life when my whole world stopped. I had become very ill, and I was unable to function or perform simple daily tasks. I was unable to work, cook, or clean, nor did I have the strength to even pay my bills. That was a very stressful time in my life. Somehow, I became very determined to regain and maintain my health. Over time my health and strength did return, and it was at that time that I vowed to take better care of myself. Whether an intense cardio workout or a stroll in the park, I discovered that any form of exercise can add value to one's health. Although working out has many physical benefits, nevertheless it could also be very challenging to find the time to exercise.

Exercise- Roadblocks

I was very active in grammar school, high school, and college. I enjoyed participating in sports, especially volleyball, basketball, and gymnastics. I also enjoyed listening to music and dancing. These activities kept me busy, energized, and in shape. Unfortunately, after college I became less active, but why? I guess my reasons were similar to many other young mothers. I was older now and working, raising children and I had no time to play sports or work out. At least that's what I used to tell myself. In addition to procrastination and unproductive busyness, I often came up with endless excuses. The following are several reasons why I was unable to work out: my job, night school, housework, my family, and extracurricular activities. I get it; life can become extremely hectic, making it difficult to find time to exercise. Some studies show that 75% of the United States population fails to even meet the minimum amount of recommended daily exercise. On average, some experts suggest that we walk a minimum of three to four times a week for at least 20-30 minutes.

Exercise - How To

Even the minimum recommended amount of exercise can be overwhelming and difficult to implement into one's active lifestyle. So how would an extremely busy individual find time to work out? On the other hand, how would a person possibly go from being a couch potato, and someone who lives a sedentary lifestyle to someone who regularly works out? Initially with a single thought, followed by a decision, and then action. At least that's how I started. Several years ago, I was not in the best of health. During that time, I made a conscious decision to first alleviate and then ultimately eliminate the pain. I then wrote out a detailed plan to lose weight. My plan consisted of several different workout techniques ranging from a simple stroll in the park to a high intense two-hour-long aerobic workout, with several variations in between. I worked out daily minor incidentals such as deciding when, where, how, and with whom to work out with.

When

Some like to work out upon awakening; they prefer to work out first thing in the morning. Whereas others prefer to work out midday or preferably later in the evening. You choose the most convenient time for you and this may be discovered through trial and error. Initially, I started to work out in the evenings, but more than often by the end of the day I was tired and would skip my workout. Present-day, I prefer to work out first thing in the morning, even if that entails me setting my alarm to get up a little earlier.

Where

Again, where to work out will vary from person to person. Some prefer to work out at the gym, at home or in the great outdoors. When the weather permits, I prefer to exercise outdoors at a park or a forest preserve. I enjoy being out in nature, in the fresh air and surrounded by beautiful trees and flowers. By doing so, I tend to extend my workout. During inclement weather, I enjoy running on my treadmill at home. By doing so, I'm able to turn my music up very loud, sing, and even maneuver a few dance-moves while on the treadmill. This makes it fun and more enjoyable, which once again encourages me to extend the amount of time I exercise. I must admit, sometimes when I'm on the treadmill I read a book, watch a movie or make phone calls. This allows me to mark off some items from my to-do list. Lastly, I enjoy going to the gym which provides opportunities, equipment, and amenities to increase one's strength and muscle tone.

How

Different workout techniques can range from very low impact to intense/high-performance workouts. Four commonly known forms of exercise are endurance, strength, flexibility, and balance, and each one has different benefits. Endurance training simply increases your heart rate. Running, swimming, and cycling are examples of endurance training. Strength training will often build muscle mass. You can build muscles by lifting weights, doing pull-ups, push-ups, or similar forms of resistance. Flexibility training is basically any form of stretching. Stretching before and or after your workout can help you avoid injuries. Three examples of flexibility exercises are toe touches, yoga, and Pilates. Balance exercises can simply help improve your balance. For example, standing on one foot, in addition to practicing martial arts.

Who

I discovered that I was able to extend my workout when I worked out with someone. Try talking while walking or jogging with a friend in the park. Invite a family member to share a gym membership. Working out with a partner may enhance, or make your workout more enjoyable, which possibly may extend the amount of time you exercise. Try to connect with someone who is just as or even more enthused and interested in some form of physical exercise as you are. When choosing someone to work out with, make sure they are reliable and dependable. It can be extremely disappointing and frustrating when friends don't show up after making a commitment to do so. Another option would be to work out with complete strangers, who nevertheless may be totally committed. Let me explain; I have a friend who likes to walk in an indoor mall. She normally arrives at 7 AM and walks for one hour, just before the retail stores open. During her one-hour walk she is able to meet and have brief conversations with different people who are also committed to walking each morning.

Exercise - Summary

Deciding when, where, how, and with whom to workout with are all important facets to consider when initially beginning or developing some form of physical activity. The key point that I would like to emphasize is to just move; get your body in motion. It doesn't have to be much; you don't have to start off by running a marathon or lifting hundred-pound weights. You don't even have to exert yourself. Start at whatever level that you are most comfortable with. A little exercise consistently can have long-lasting, and beneficial results.

For several years I would arrive at work on average, 30 to 45 minutes early. I worked in a large hospital-type facility with long hallways and corridors. This allowed me an opportunity to get in several laps before my shift started. Initially I would often walk with several of my co-workers. We often walked at a moderate to fast pace. But there was one co-worker who walked very slowly; let's call her Ms. C.P. I and several of my co-workers would often pass her once or twice before she completed one lap. I thought her leisurely, almost idol pace was not very physically beneficial. At that time in my life, I thought you had to exert a certain amount of energy in order to obtain any physical benefits from your workout. I was so wrong. After several weeks Ms. C.P shared with her co-workers that she went to visit her doctor. Her doctor informed her that her vitals and her overall health had slightly improved over the past few weeks. This motivated her to continue to walk. Over several months her health significantly improved. She lost weight, became more energetic, and she was able to get off some of her prescription drugs which she had taken for years. She attributed her improved quality of life to her persistent walking. In short, persistence equals progress. In addition to increasing my physical activities, I also changed my diet. I began to eating more nutritious meals and drinking more water to maintain adequate hydration. Over the years the results have been life-changing; I feel and look better.

I would like to conclude this section by sharing some of the following amazing benefits of exercising: increase the quality of one's life, promoting relaxation, better sleep, increased energy, and decreased anxiety, stress, and feelings of depression. Exercise also increases the heart rate, which pumps more oxygen to the brain, which improves brain function such as increased memory, one's attention span, and focus. Overall exercise improves the quality of both one's mental, and physical well-being.

Educate- Description

To educate is basically the ability to obtain and or impart knowledge and insight. I was brought up in a household where education was highly stressed. My mom and especially my dad always stressed and emphasized the importance of education. Although my parents never went to college, nevertheless they were both wise and strong advocates of higher education. My father was always seeking knowledge and new information in an attempt to increase his income and improve the lives of his family members. Throughout my father's lifetime, he enrolled in several trade schools and attended seminars which led to his proficiency and expertise in many areas. He was a highly skilled craft man working within the industries of tool and die, auto mechanic, carpentry, masonry, construction, real estate, and sales. There was one other school that my father attended that helped pave the way for him to achieve some of his greatest success. That was the school of hard knocks.

For several years my mother worked at a lamp company until the company decided to relocate and move out of state. Soon after that, my mom decided to enroll in a nursing program. She was actually going to sign up for nursing school! The entire family was shocked. Mom was now in her 50s and she had not stepped foot in a classroom since high school. The class required that she learn and memorize several medical terms, complete several hours of training, and participate in a medical practicum within a local hospital. I thought it would all be too overwhelming for her. Nevertheless, she graduated at the top of her class. I was extremely proud of her. I can still vividly see her sitting there on the front row of her graduation day, smiling from ear to ear. She wore a bright, crisp and neatly pressed white nurse's uniform along with her nurse's cap. Her feet were adorned with her brand-new white shoes, which were purchased specifically for that day. Both my parents focused on completing their educational goals, and they encouraged their children to do the same. They knew a college education would provide an opportunity to obtain knowledge, information, and insight. I took their advice at heart and discovered that continuous learning has great potential to elevate one's life. Within the same vein, I discovered that there were also roadblocks to higher education.

Educate - Roadblocks

The entire family, including my mom, was extremely proud of her accomplishments. She had completed months of arduous studies and training to complete her nursing program. Unfortunately, some of my mother's classmates were unable to complete the program. Time and money were the two main culprits. This is still very much true today. Many individuals are often too busy to find time to go back to college or even simply pick up a book to read. Then there's the other factor of money. Sometimes we may simply not have the finances to fund a four-year college education. Then there is the fear factor. Even if we have the money and the time, fear can be a huge hindrance.

When my children became adults, I seriously decided to obtain my bachelor's degree. The idea of returning to school created fear. I was older now and I was fearful that I would not be able to keep up with the classwork. And we were now living in a world of advanced technology. Mind you; I was that individual who fought to hold on to my flip phone as long as possible. With that being said, I remember gathering up enough courage to meet with a guidance counselor and register for a class. The counselor informed me that I needed to take a specific math class in order to graduate. The book required for this class was entitled: "Mathematical and analytical equations of amortization." The title of the book so scared me that fear and doubt immediately flooded my entire being. "There is no way I can pass this class." those were the words I mumbled under my breath as I hesitantly purchased the book.

Educate - How To

Once I exited the bookstore, I slowed my pace and suddenly stopped in the middle of the hallway. While standing there I slowly glanced down at the math book and began flipping through the pages. I thought, "It's going to take a miracle in order for me to pass this class." Immediately, at that moment I again felt fear over power me. Feeling dejected, I turned around and headed back in the direction of the bookstore in order to return the book and drop the class. With the bookstore, only a few feet in front of me I again slowed my pace and stopped. Somehow, I was able to block out the chatter of the many students around me as they rushed past me, heading to their next class. As the halls cleared, I just stood there. Then I heard a familiar voice. The voice said, "You can do this." I remember years ago when someone gave me advice that changed and altered my life. I often think about that amazing and life-changing moment. They boldly shared with me the following advice; "Whenever you are afraid, do it afraid." Whatever it is that makes you fearful, don't allow the fear to stop you. Just do it afraid. I have now practiced doing things afraid for years, and what I have discovered is that the more I do things afraid, the braver I become and the fear dissipates.

Maybe you're not afraid; maybe you simply don't have the time. I get it, life happens. You barely have enough time to go to work, manage your household, your relationships, and what little time you have left for self-care. Rearranging your schedule to create and or free up time to implement a new activity can be challenging. But nevertheless, it can be so rewarding and worth it. Initially, I found myself sacrificing some of my sleep time in order to rearrange my schedule. I would often get up early in the morning in an attempt to remove some things from my to-do list. This freed up time later in the day to attend a class and/or study.

Granted, fear nor time may not be an issue for you. You might not possess the finances to fund a college education. If you currently cannot pursue a four-year college education, then start with a community college. The classes are often smaller, more intimate, and less expensive. If attending a community college is not an option then consider your local library. Apply for a library card if you don't have one, then take the initiative to research a topic of your choice. Does that sound like too much work? Then simply check out a book, a periodical, an educational CD, or an educational video. Are you unable to get to your local library? If so then choose to watch the historical, educational, and documentary channels on your television. You don't have a television? Then download educational apps on your phone. You don't have a phone? Then when friends and family members come over ask them to share their expertise or whatever educational information they may possess. You don't have friends and family members? Then visit the recesses of your mind, and delve deep within your subconscious. Search for and tap into any neural network of your brain housing any collegiate information you may have learned many years ago. Then pull that information up into your conscious mind and mix it with your imagination to create the simplest form of learning. The point I'm trying to get at is that if there is a will there's a way.

Education- Summary

The idea here is to obtain information. How much information you obtain, and how you apply that information depends on you. My main focus is not to stress a classroom education, although I do encourage one. My main focus here is to encourage and motivate learning through whichever avenue that is most convenient for you. Sitting within a structured classroom may not be convenient, nor your desire. It may be more convenient to take an online course. Others may simply be able to read a few pages from a book each night. Or you may simply choose to listen to audiobooks while driving in your car. Wherever you are able to obtain information, do so to the best of your ability.

Exposure - Description

When you woke up this morning and immediately opened your eyes, what did you see; a ceiling, a spouse, a child, a pillow, or possibly a wall? If you left your house, where did you go; to the park, the gym, a restaurant, your place of employment, or possibly the grocery store? How did you get there; did you drive, walk, ride a bicycle, take public transportation, or call an Uber? Upon arrival, what did you do, who did you see, and how long did you stay? Take a moment, and reflect on your daily routine. Where do you often go, and whom do you often associate with? Your answer will reveal what you are exposed to on a daily basis.

Exposure roughly means open to view, not protected or shielded. Exposure also means to experience something and or gather knowledge. Your continuous exposure to certain things, environments, people, and circumstances has the ability and the potential to impact your decisions and ultimately the direction of your life. What are you exposed to on a daily basis? Are you exposed to the greater things of life? For example, do you own your own home? Do you have the ability to sleep in a comfortable bed each night, or are you exposed to less then? For example, are you exposed to an overcrowded, one-bedroom apartment? Maybe you pay rent to live in one single room or the ability to sleep on someone's couch. Is it possible that you make your bed in the back seat of your car? I recall times in my life when I was exposed to less; less money, less opportunities, and less health. Over the years I have made great attempts to expose myself to the greater things of life and hope to avoid stagnation, complacency, and becoming comfortable with less. In Spite of my many efforts, I inevitably ran into several roadblocks.

Exposure - Roadblocks

A lack of finances and ignorance were two of the main roadblocks which prevented me from experiencing greater exposure in my life.

Let's first address ignorance. I simply just didn't know that there were influential people, beautiful places, and greater things that existed and possibly possessed the potential to increase my life by simply being exposed to them. Have you ever felt as though you were stuck? Possibly stuck in a certain living environment, stuck in a marriage, or stuck at a job that you didn't like? And if so, why? Why is it that we continue to live within a cramped space, live in a toxic marriage, or keep company with toxic people? Oftentimes people desire to change their immediate surroundings but are unable to do so. I vividly remember giving birth to my first-born son. A week later my son and I left the hospital; both frail and fragile, we headed home. The home was a two-bedroom overcrowded apartment on the southside of Chicago within one of the less developed and unkept neighborhoods. This was not where I wanted to raise my son, but I had nowhere else to go. I simply couldn't afford to move. A lack of adequate finances created a lack of options that limited my choices. I often thought about the many things I could accomplish if I only had more money. More money would have created more opportunities to expand my child's exposure to greater things in this world.

Exposure - How To

Your finances may currently prevent or limit your exposure to more. Maybe you live in an apartment but hope to own your own home one day. Maybe your dream is to purchase a more spacious home. Maybe you desire to purchase a car or a second one. Could it be that your finances prevent you from doing so? If that may be your current situation, then I encourage you to "window shop." Window shopping is often described as the activity of looking at something on display, usually within a storefront window. The intention is not to purchase but to admire and/ or possibly purchase at a later date when funds become available. I vividly remember my childhood and my oldest sister Mary, who truly enjoyed shopping. She would often take me with her whenever she went shopping. At that time, I did not know the power of window shopping. Now when I suggest that you window shop, it's more than just looking in the window of your favorite department store. "Window shopping" is also a term I use to basically explain the process of exposing yourself to something or someone greater. The idea is to intentionally expose yourself to more, to greater in spite of the possibility that you may not currently be able to purchase or secure greater. "Window shopping" has the ability to create temporary exposure. This limited or temporary exposure has the ability to spark creativity which can increase one's passion and desire for more. And with that increased desire, one's innovation is enlarged, and new ideas are sparked. This can lead to new and creative ways on how not only expose yourself to greater but also how to possess greater.

I learned how to be more intentional when I attempted to expose myself to the finer things of life. For example, if you cannot afford the car of your dreams, test drive one. If you can't afford the house with four bedrooms, 4 1/2 baths, a large kitchen, a den, and other amenities, then call a local realtor, and schedule a walk-through. Although you may not have the down payment, go to the open house. Do you have a desire to go back to school although you currently may not have the resources or the money? Then take a tour of a nearby college campus. And it wouldn't hurt to schedule an appointment to speak with an advisor or counselor about your collegiate interest. What is your dream vacation? Would you like to spend a week or two on the beautiful island of Maui Hawaii but currently can't afford it? Then I encourage you to google Hawaii and its neighboring islands. Research the beautiful islands and even speak to a travel agent about popular tourist sites. The idea is to expose yourself as often as possible to your desired dreams as you strive and work toward accomplishing and reaching the actual dream itself. In a nutshell that's descriptive of how you "window shop". Lastly, I would like to emphasize the fact that exposing yourself to more has the ability to inspire and increase one's motivation for greater.

Exposure - Summary

The main point I would like to highlight from this section is that exposure equals preference. Some years ago, while attending a motivational seminar, I recall one of the speakers making a profound statement. He eloquently explained that whatever someone is continuously exposed to, they will over time become comfortable with and eventually prefer it. Whatever it may be; wealth or poverty, health or sickness, maybe peace or war. As I reflect back on the many memories and events of my life, I discovered this statement to be true.

Whatever it is that you are exposed to on a regular basis, whether negative or positive, more or less, you will gradually prefer it, accept it, and incorporate it into your life. The following are three things that tremendously helped me enlarge my exposure to greater: daily affirmations, "window shopping." and using my creative imagination. I had often imagined how it would feel on that dream vacation and becoming a millionaire. I imagined how it would feel riding in my dream car and how I would feel on that dream date with that tall, handsome, wealthy gentleman. I also imagined the excitement I would feel running my own business. Many of us can't imagine creating and owning a business or living in a beautiful lavish home, driving luxury cars, or taking elaborate five-star vacations. To be honest we don't dream of more because we often think we don't deserve more or we can't obtain more. And if you believe you cannot obtain more, then it is highly probable that you will not. In summary, whatever you are routinely exposed to has the potential to become your normal. It's such a slippery slope because we often tolerate our normal. Finally, what you tolerate, you won't change.

Chapter 13
Live,
Leave,
Level
Up

Live - Description

What is life if you can't enjoy it? Throughout my mother's lifetime, I must have heard her ask this question at least a thousand times or more. It was her way of encouraging people to enjoy their life. This question had actually become one of her many inspiring mantras. My mother enjoyed her life, and often encouraged others to do the same. She worked a full-time job, was a caring and supportive wife, ran an efficient household, raised five children, and volunteered within the community. Although mom had many responsibilities, I vividly remember her creating opportunities which the entire family would enjoy. She enjoyed both cooking and eating. She loved to laugh, tell jokes, dance, travel, entertain, and celebrate each phase of life. My mother would often encourage me to live my life to the fullest. She would often motivate me not to put things off or postpone doing something which I truly enjoy. A song writer once wrote, "If you get a chance to sit it out, or dance; dance." He is basically trying to convey that if you get the opportunity to enjoy life, take it. What is it that makes you happy, energetic, vibrant, and alive? Whatever it may be, then do more of it. We normally get one shot at this thing called life. Take the time and enjoy it.

Live - Roadblocks

Let's investigate some roadblocks, some things that might prevent you from enjoying your life. Can you think of any? Let me be the first to raise my hand. I must admit for many years I did not live my best life, nor did I take the opportunities to do so. I'm still in the process of going after better in many areas of my life. I did not know

I was not living my best life, nor did I know how to. I had become comfortable living a less than fulfilled life. There were several reasons why. I believe busyness was the number one reason why I missed opportunities to enjoy life. As a wife, a mother of five school-age children, and working a full-time job did not leave as much time as I would have liked for relaxation and recreational activities. Sickness and poor health were other roadblocks. Have you ever had the desire to take a vacation or just do something fun but you were physically unable? Yes, I have and yes, I was unable to do so. In addition to illness, lack of finances, hurt, bitterness, unforgiveness and other similar obstacles all prevented me from enjoying a more fulfilled life. Are you not living your best life because of similar reasons? Have you settled for possibly just going to work each day, dreading Mondays, and looking forward to Friday? If so, you're not alone; millions of people live similar lifestyles. You need to know there's more to life than just working five days out of the week. There are several ways to overcome obstacles that prevent you from living your best life.

Live - How To

So how do you live your best life? You must first make a conscious decision to do so, and that is exactly what I did. I recall many years ago thumbing through a magazine and I came across a self-care article. The author suggested that busy moms take themselves out to dinner. I took his advice and I did exactly that. I went to my favorite restaurant and ordered my favorite dish. After the entrée, I began to read one of my favorite books which I brought with me as I enjoyed a slice of apple pie, two scoops of vanilla ice cream and a cup of hot green tea. Throughout the evening my waitress would sheepishly refill my empty teacup as she tried not to disturb my reading. I truly enjoyed my meal, my book, and my undisturbed time. I left that restaurant feeling refreshed. After that pleasant evening, I started to strategically and purposefully carve out more time to enjoy similar activities. Often mothers are extremely busy caring for their spouse and their children. Although marriage and motherhood can be very rewarding, they can also be very stressful. Both moms and dads need "me time." When you take time to enjoy your life it can eliminate stress and anxiety. But I get it, sometimes it's not that simple. You presently may not be able to afford to eat out, go to the movies, or take a vacation. The idea here is to take the time to spend time doing the things you like and spend time with people whom you like. You may have to come up with money-free creative ways to enjoy yourself, but the effort would be worth it.

Anger, bitterness, and hatred are massive roadblocks to your ability to enjoy life. My ex-husband often complained about everything, which led to frustration and several arguments. In addition, he would often say or do something that was mean and hurtful. Afterwards, I would often develop a grudge and or unforgiveness toward him. When you harbor and hold onto hurt and unforgiveness it has the ability to consume your focus. When your focus is consumed with hatred and hurt you truly can't enjoy your life. It was that knowledge that led me to make a conscious decision to forgive him and anyone else who had ever intentionally hurt and mistreated me. Developing the ability to forgive allowed me to shift my focus from hurt and bitterness toward people and circumstances to joy and peace in my life.

Maybe you're not in the best of health, or maybe you have an illness that prevents you from truly enjoying your life. There was a time in my life that I was sick, extremely sick and I could only think about the pain and how to relieve it. During that unfortunate time, I was unable to think about the simplest enjoyments of my life. My thoughts were constantly consumed with eliminating or at least lessening the pain I was experiencing on a daily basis. Maybe you can relate? So how do you get rid of the pain? The following is a list of simple ideas to help improve one's health: proper sleep, exercise, meditation, eating nutritious foods, eliminating stress, laughter, drinking plenty of water, avoiding illegal drugs, abstaining from smoking cigarettes, and excessive alcohol consumption. Lastly, making routine doctor visits is extremely beneficial. I know this list may seem simple to some but others may find it extremely difficult to implement these healthy activities into their daily routine. I did. Years ago, I found it very difficult to do simple exercises, get adequate sleep, let alone eat a piece of fruit or some green vegetables. That is, of course until my health failed me. I remember a time when I found myself in constant pain. It took me several years to figure out how to eliminate that constant discomfort. The best way to avoid sickness is to implement healthy preventative measures on a daily basis. In other words, on a daily basis do something that will increase the quality of your life no matter how large or small. The goal is to make more healthy choices. Benjamin Franklin once eloquently stated, "An ounce of prevention is worth a pound of cure." In other words, it's better to initiate and take precautionary measures instead of dealing with the results of not doing so.

Live - Summary

Do things you've never done before and it may surprise you; you may actually enjoy it. Or maybe do some of those things you have been putting off. For example, connect with an old friend, call your mother, take a vacation, go fishing, go to a party, or say I'm sorry. Do whatever it is that eliminates stress and makes you happy. Take time to do whatever it is that makes you feel alive. Don't live your whole life, then get near the end and have nothing but regret. My mom used to always say take time to stop and smell the roses. It's an old cliché that basically means to stop and take time out of your busy life and enjoy and appreciate it and the people with whom you share it with. Life goes by so quickly; it's like a vapor. How often do people find themselves on their deathbed with many regrets? They often feel as though they truly didn't live the life they wanted, so they settled, compromised, or gave up? Oftentimes you don't live your life to the fullest because you are afraid to step out and do something different. We often just float through life, neglecting, and putting things off. My mother often encouraged her family to take each opportunity to enjoy their life. You get one shot at this thing called life, so enjoy it! In summary, and in the words of my mother, I once again ask," What is life, if you can't enjoy it?"

Leave - Description

Have you ever waited a portion of your life for someone to return who had abandoned, walked away, or simply just left you possibly years ago? Please, allow me to be the first to raise my hand. Yes, I waited for several years for my then- husband to return. Now initially he did not actually physically pack up and leave. He had mentally left his wife and children many years before the word divorce was even uttered. Yes, he went to work and came home but he wasn't "all there." he wasn't totally present; his focus and his thoughts were elsewhere. While standing there waiting, I was hopeful and prayerful that he would one day return home, both physically and mentally. He never did. But when he actually packed his bags and physically moved out, I found myself faced with the inevitable. It was time to leave; it was now time for me to leave a position, a prostate, and a mindset of waiting. But even more importantly, it was time for me to totally let him go. I had to mentally allow him the freedom to physically leave. Leave is the act of walking away and separating yourself from someone or something. Divorce or temporary separation can be devastating and extremely painful. Oftentimes we try to avoid hardship and stick together. Sometimes that creates a greater hardship. This idea of leaving has twofold; allow yourself to leave, and secondly, allow individuals the same freedom to leave. Don't try to hold on to people who no longer want to be with you. Although it sounds simple enough to actually give someone the freedom to walk away, nevertheless it can be difficult to do.

Leave - Roadblocks

Why would anyone stay with someone who is abusive? Why would a wife stay with her husband who no longer loves her and who is often rude, disrespectful, and hateful? Why wouldn't they just simply pack their bags, walk out and leave? Yes, that seems simple enough; just pack your bags, walk out and leave. But it's not just that simple; at least it wasn't for me. I initially did not leave him because of fear, finances, feelings, friends, and my faith.

Fear

Initially, I did not leave because of fear. It was the fear of the unknown. I had never been divorced, and I didn't know what to expect. I was fearful that I would not be able to make it without him. I depended on him financially, mentally, and physically. I often thought how would I be able to survive? As our lives began to move in opposite directions, I could feel the tension and stress build. The world that I once knew had drastically changed. And I was afraid to face this new world that I was now forced into. It became very apparent that my world was more intertwined with his as we both began to pull apart. Being pulled in opposite directions was both painful and fearful. I must admit that despite the anguish and the abuse, I tried to stay with him and change him. It was all in an attempt to avoid the unknown which created massive fear.

Finances

Some experts say that finances are one of the main reasons people get divorced. I agree, but I have also discovered that finances are also one reason why people avoid divorce. While going through my divorce I spoke with several ladies who were also in toxic marriages and felt stuck. Many of them shared with me that they were unable to afford the cost of a divorce. They simply could not afford a lawyer. They couldn't afford to pay the total amount of the mortgage or rent in addition to legal fees. Without adequate finances and often time without hope they stayed. And many of them who did leave remained married although separated for months and even years.

Feelings

I didn't leave because I still had some feelings for him. I used to think that I possessed enough love for both of us. There was a time when he used to make me feel happy, but over the years that drastically changed. He, more often actually made me feel the opposite of anything that remotely resembled happiness. But nevertheless, I attempted to hold onto any small fragments of warm fuzzy feelings of love that had long passed.

Friends

Sometimes family and friends interfere with one's decision to get a divorce, especially when young children are involved. I have heard people encourage women to stay in toxic and abusive marriages for the sake of the children. Exactly what does that mean? "Stay for the sake of the children." Should a child be made to stay in a broken home and watch their father verbally and physically abuse their mother? Sometimes good friends give bad advice.

Faith

I was brought up in a Baptist household and we were taught that divorce was taboo. I was taught that if you get married you should stay married. Despite the abuse and mistreatment, I was encouraged to love and support my husband. This is what I believed, and this is what I had attempted to do for years.

Leave- How To

I had little money in my pocket, nowhere to go, and I was reluctant to face the world apart from my marriage. The truth was that I didn't want to leave him, and I didn't know how to; but he did. He knew exactly how to leave me. He had set before me an example; he first secured other living arrangements. He then organized his mail and shredded all unwanted letters and documents. Thirdly, he gradually removed his clothes from the closet and items from his dresser drawers. Lastly, and with very few words spoken, he packed his toiletries and other needed items and moved out. It wasn't until months later that I followed his example. The first thing I did was to accept the fact that he was gone and that he was not coming back. That same day I made a conscious decision that it was now time to go. I had reached a point in my life where I now valued my safety and sanity more than false security with him. I still didn't know what the future would hold but I had a newfound strength to face my fears and whatever challenges may lay ahead.

Fear

Someone once shared with me some powerful truths and principles about fear. I immediately applied them to my life and still practice them today. These principles yielded positive results. These truths helped me conquer many of my fears. The following are three life-changing principles of fear: when afraid, do it anyway. Secondly, Faith and fear cannot reside within the same space and time, and finally, spoken words override unspoken thoughts. Whenever I begin to have a negative thought, I immediately address it and intentionally attempt to think positive thoughts. This act would often prevent negative thoughts from consuming me and intensifying my fears. I refused to allow negative thoughts to wash over me. I would also verbally speak out loud encouraging and positive quotes, which would often interrupt and abate negative thoughts. I would also reach out to a selected group of individuals to encourage me as well. Having motivating conversations with positive individuals in addition to reciting verbal affirmations on a daily basis abated many of my fears. Now there were days when fear unexpectedly gripped and took control of my thoughts. In those days, I had to act and behave opposite to my feelings and thoughts. For example, some years ago, I made a decision to go back to school. As August approached, I began to experience much fear and seriously contemplated not continuing my education. Somehow, I was able to act the opposite of my fearful thoughts. So early one Monday morning, with wobbly knees, shaking hands and with small beads of perspiration forming near my hairline and within the folds of my elbow I walked into Roosevelt University and registered for a class. Before I conclude this section on fear, let me end with two Bible verses which tremendously helped me to overcome fear: "For God hath not given us the spirit of fear; but of power, and of love, and of a sound mind." ,2 Timothy 1:7 (NKJV) and "I can do all things through Christ who strengthens me." , Philippians 4:13 (NKJV)

Finances

Although my faith had increased, my finances had not. Although I worked a full-time job my salary was not enough to cover the mortgage, utilities, incidentals, and lawyer fees. I had credit card debt, and little savings in the bank. Unfortunately, this is the scenario for many women who are on the verge or going through the process of divorce. They want to leave and some need to leave but they can't. While going through this hardship, I was fortunate to have a mother and a younger brother to assist me both mentally and financially. And I understand that many may not have family members who can support them financially. So here I have to be brutally honest; if my mother and brother did not step up to help, I honestly don't know what I would have done. In lieu of that, there are programs, non-for-profit organizations, and support groups which offer financial assistance for women in need. I did apply for one of these programs and discovered there was a long waiting list. They made me jump through hoops as they deliberately attempted to make me feel less than and undeserving because of my financial situation. This is unfortunate but this is how women might be treated when seeking financial assistance. An older lady once told me many years ago to put money aside, just in case I get a divorce. I wish I had taken her advice. I know many women can't receive this advice because we get married and hope it will last a lifetime. Today statistics show that on the average, more than 50% of marriages end in divorce. Just food for thought.

Feelings

I recall the day my feelings for him drastically changed. I can pinpoint the exact moment it occurred. It was late; it was actually after midnight. I was at work and he was at home. We were talking on the phone, and it was something he said, and even more pertinent, it was something he did not say. At the end of that conversation, it was as if a lightbulb came on, and I had an epiphany. With tears in my eyes, I thought, and even softly uttered the words out loud, "What's the point? This man does not care, and he no longer loves me." And I knew every woman deserves to be loved by her husband. Once I accepted the fact that he no longer loved me, my affection toward him drastically declined. The thrill was gone. Sometimes we stay in marriages in hopes to rekindle or ignite a flame that had burnt out years ago. Figuratively speaking that flame that had once burned passionately within our relationship had been doused with the water of rejection, disrespect, and abuse. That once blaze was now extinguished forever.

Friends

Whom do you often seek advice from? Before you make a serious decision, do you first call your parents, your spouse, your children, your friends, or possibly your pastor? Over the years I have sought advice from all of them, and I have received both good and bad advice. When seeking the advice of others, consider their motive, and their expertise and check to see if they possibly have an agenda for offering certain advice. When friends and or family members offer advice just don't take and apply their advice simply because you feel obligated or because you have known them a long time. You may be tempted to take their advice because they are good people. Sometimes good people give bad advice. Over the years I have learned to consider and be mindful of the advice of friends who profess to have my best interest at heart. Actually, I'm now more mindful of everyone who offers advice. Lastly, consider the advice offered, weigh your options, pray about it, seek Gods' face, and then make a decision and act.

Faith

I have been reading the Bible for most of my life. Only about a decade ago, I discovered that someone within my family tree misinterpreted some parts of the scriptures. And that misinterpretation was handed down generation after generation. For years women within my family were taught to support their husbands in good times and bad times and in the worst of times. This is what I wholeheartedly believed when growing up and this is what I practice within my marriage. Now I can understand and accept this premise only when a husband and wife are fighting together toward a common goal or against a common enemy. But when a husband is physically fighting his wife, that is unacceptable. Domestic abuse is ungodly. Mental and physical abuse of any kind should not be tolerated. Let me end this section with a couple of Bible verses: "Husbands, love your wives, and do not be harsh with them." , Colossians 3:19 (ESV) "But if the unbelieving partner separates, let it be so. In such cases the brother or sister is not enslaved. God has called you to peace." ,1 Corinthians 7:15 (ESV) "Likewise, husbands, live with your wives in an understanding way, showing honor to the woman as the weaker vessel, since they are heirs with you of the grace of life, so that your prayers may not be hindered." ,1 Peter 3:7 (ESV)

Leave - Summary

In summation of this section please let me say, and allow me to make this perfectly clear that I am not one to advocate for divorce on minor issues. Maybe your husband leaves the toilet seat up or leaves his underwear on the floor. Maybe your wife doesn't keep the house clean or cook a hot meal every day. Although these behaviors may be irritating and can cause frustration to some but may not to others. But I do not believe they warrant divorce proceedings. Marriage is often hard work, but nevertheless, I also believe it's worth fighting for. I do believe marriage is God-ordained. It's a beautiful thing when a man and a woman come together with common goals to faithfully love, cherish and support each other as they fight together to build a home and a future.

On the other hand, I do not believe marriage is worth fighting for at the expense of a spouse's physical and mental well-being. I left that marriage both mentally, emotionally, and physically drained. I was once that individual who would encourage people to stay in a toxic marriage. I used to encourage couples to work together, go to counseling, and make great attempts to stay together. I didn't take into consideration that sometimes people will never change. I didn't take into consideration alcoholism, drugs, and other addictive agents. Neither did I take into consideration that philandering can become addictive. The impact and the power of leaving, or simply walking away and or allowing other people to walk away can be life-changing and even possibly save your life. It saved my life.

Level Up - Description

I recall a decade-plus ago, my family, and I moved into a house, which was built from the ground up. This was the first time I had ever done anything like this. It was all new and exciting. To my surprise it was quickly built, we moved in, and I immediately started to decorate each room. Within less than a year, we had the house fully furnished, painted, wallpapered, and color-coordinated to our liking. I found myself one day home alone, sitting on the couch, just looking around, feeling both grateful and appreciative. I also felt a sense of accomplishment. I really felt as if I had arrived at a place in my life where I could live out the remainder of my life within the four walls of this house and surrounded by my family. I thought to myself, "I made it." "This is it." I thought to myself that this would be the house where my children, grandchildren, friends, and family members would gather for the holidays to celebrate each other and events. I felt as if I had reached a comfortable level in my life. I didn't have many other goals or dreams, nor had I aspired to take my life to new levels. And I was ok with it.

Back then, I could not conceive or grasp the concept of "leveling up." For many years, I was basically stuck on one level, which resembled the following pattern; get up, go to work, come home, cook, clean, pay bills and repeat. I had become comfortable and settled for a revolving lifestyle of familiarity. To become stuck, stagnated, and never reaching for the greater has the ability to create a mundane comfort zone. It wasn't until many years later that I came to realize the importance and the impact of simply aspiring to obtain greater. Leveling up is possessing a mindset of never settling; it's the act of continually striving to improve, increase, elevate, and become better in each area of your life.

Level Up - Roadblocks

Is it possible that you have fallen into a rut, a mundane, or a predictable lifestyle? Has there been any increase, or improvement in any areas of your life within the past few months or even within the past year? Is it possible that you have become stagnated, stuck on the same or a lower level within a certain area of your life? If so, then what is it that holds you to that level and prevents you from achieving more, and obtaining increase? What's preventing you from leveling up? Think about that question for a moment. Then take out a piece of paper and write down your answer. While writing, reflect on those things that you have always talked about, those things that you once said that you would complete by next week, next month, or for sure before next year. What are those things that you have been putting off and postponing to complete? Your answers may surprise you. When I initially sat down to write out my list, I was shocked, disappointed, and even somewhat angry with myself because I had allowed so much time to go by without reaching many of my goals. I was somewhat frustrated because after so many years, I had not seen an increase, nor had I advanced in many areas of my life. That one thought led me to write out another list, a list of obstacles to my success. After much thought and deliberation, the following list of words appeared in bold dark letters, juxtaposed in one column onto my writing pad: fear, finances, familiarity, family, friends, and faith

Fear

We often don't experience an increase in our lives due to fear. Oftentimes fear is one of our biggest obstacles to success. Individuals will not start a business, go back to school, or even buy a house because they are fearful that something will go wrong and they are often fearful that they will fail at their attempts. Fear can be extremely crippling, which can lead to a mindset of constant doubt. If fear is not addressed or dealt with, it can paralyze you.

Finances

Many of the world's population are broke, poor, or destitute. That is the sentiment of the majority of our population. Then there are others, and although they may possess an adequate amount of money, it never seems to be enough. The lack of or the insufficient amount of money will often prevent or interfere with your ability to pursue and obtain greater levels of success.

Familiarity

Have you fallen into a comfort zone of familiarity? Have you been doing something a certain way for so long that you absolutely refuse to change or do it differently? If so then you have become "stuck in your ways." That's a term my mother used to use when describing individuals who refuse to do anything different. I know an individual who for many years lived a simple life. He didn't have hobbies; he wasn't interested in traveling or social gatherings. He basically went to work, came back home, ate, watched television, went to bed, and got up the next day to repeat his routine. And repeat it he did for the next 35-40 years. I get it; it can be extremely difficult to break old habits. Old habits can stifle your innovation, and your ability to create and experience new things.

Friends

The following is one of my youngest daughter's many mantras; "Bad Company corrupts good character." It basically means if you hang out with negative and toxic individuals it's highly likely that you will start to exhibit similar behaviors. If you continuously associate with individuals who lack motivation, drive or strive for greater, most likely you will be more inclined to settle for less. Truth be told, sometimes friends and family members secretly don't want to see you excel. And often as quiet as kept, they don't want you to do better than them. Possibly unbeknown to you, they will covertly motivate you to live on a lower level, at least on a level directly beneath them.

Faith

Sometimes an individual's up-bringing, beliefs, and or faith will prevent them from desiring or aspiring for more out of life. Sometimes an individual's faith encourages meekness and less than. They will deliberately avoid living in a big house, driving a nice car, and wearing nice clothes. They shun any form of prosperity. I once heard a minister share his testimony concerning his faith. He shared a time in his life when he believed God wanted him to be meek and humble. He went on to share a difficult time in his life when he didn't have much money or food. During that time, he and his wife had not eaten in days. Somehow, he believed that it was the will of God.

Level Up - How To

Whether it's your fears, deep-seated beliefs, friends or family members giving you negative advice, a lack of finances, or simply your inability to step out of your comfort zone, these roadblocks must be addressed in order to exhibit increase or simply the next level up. But how? How do we overcome what sometimes appear to be insurmountable roadblocks? Let's first address fear.

Fear

Fear was my greatest obstacle to my increase. I was afraid that it wouldn't work, and I was afraid of what people would think and say, so I often did nothing. For several years that remained true until one day, someone told me that whenever I was afraid, I should do the one thing that I'm afraid of. In other words, if you are afraid to do something, do it anyway. Do it afraid. That small piece of advice changed my thought processes and changed the projection of my life. I took their advice at heart and I started to do things while afraid. I discovered that the more I did things afraid, the braver I became. Over the years I came to discover that fear will dissipate and significantly shrink when continuous courage and action are repeated. I would often reference the following two Bible verses which tremendously helped abate many of my fears: "I can do all things through Christ who strengthens me.", Philippians 4:13 (KJV), "For God hath not given us the spirit of fear; but of power, and of love, and of a sound mind." ,2 Timothy 1:7 (KJV)

Finances

In succession, I believe inadequate finances are the second-largest roadblocks to one's ability to level up. We often hear people say "I just don't have enough money." I was one of those individuals, and that was my exact sentiment for several years. That is, until one day, I heard a speaker offer some financial advice. He said spend less money than you earn on a continuous basis. Although simple, it was sound advice. I took his advice and I applied it to my monthly budget. And over time I was able to eliminate some debt and watched my savings grow. As my savings grew, I was motivated to find ways to increase my income. I thought about the following opportunities: ask for a raise, secure a second job, online marketing, sales, or start a business. However, you choose to increase your income, remember the basic premise is to spend less than what you earn on a continuous basis. As your money increases, so will your opportunities to purchase, travel, and reach goals within every area of your life.

Familiarity

If you want something different, you're going to have to do something different. Doing something different can be quite difficult to accomplish. It often requires that we step out of our comfort zones. What are some of the things you normally wouldn't do but have a desire to do? Maybe you would like to go bungee jumping or skydiving but never had the courage to do so. Recently my daughter was invited to go skydiving with some friends. When the day came to jump, everyone except one other person had canceled and decided not to jump for whatever reason. I believe they chose not to jump because it was so unfamiliar and that unfamiliarity had created fear. I asked my daughter how she was able to jump out of a plane for the first time? She informed me that it was something that she had always wanted to do. Secondly, she verbally and mentally kept telling herself, "I can do this, I can do this." And she then jumped. Maybe you prefer to do something less extreme. Whatever it may be, do something out of the ordinary. I employ you to do something different. Even if it's as simple as taking a different route to work, buying something you would have never considered purchasing, or simply rolling out of the opposite side of your bed. This might seem quite small and insignificant, but the main idea is to do something different.

Friends

I once heard Billionaire entrepreneurs, rags to riches, and extraordinaire Jay Z ask the question, "What's better than one black billionaire?" The answer was two. When I heard this, I was moved and something stirred within me. I was immediately motivated and inspired to first become a millionaire, but I had no idea as to how to accomplish it. One of my mentors once told me that if I desired to become a millionaire, then I needed to get around other millionaires. At that time none of my friends, family members, or associates was millionaires, nor did they desire to be millionaires. Truth be told, many of them desired to live paycheck to paycheck for the remainder of their lives. Unfortunately, their lifestyle and financial desires greatly influenced me to do the same. Something had to change, and I needed to get around some different people. I remember the day things drastically changed for me. I met a young lady. Although she was not a millionaire at the time, she had a millionaire's mindset. I met her at a financial seminar and had an opportunity to speak with her on several occasions. I don't know what it was, but it was something different about her. It might have been that stern but passionate look in her eyes. It could have been her astute posture or her confident body language which drew the attention of many in the room. Maybe it was her confident inflections in her voice. After the seminar, I went on to stay connected with this young lady and others from the seminar. These new connections and friendships motivated me to take my life to new levels. If you currently do not have friends or family members who are millionaires then get around people who have millionaire mindsets. Lastly, read about and study the lifestyle of wealthy individuals.

MILDRED "MICKEY" GIVENS

Faith

There are several bible verses that speak about meekness. Sometimes people interpret these verses as living below their means and not to seeking greater. Some people believe they are more holy or godly when they possess less. I for one never interpreted any of the scriptures as such. But I have come across scriptures that encourage abundance and increase. It's these scriptures that I choose to continue to focus on. And by doing so I am encouraged and motivated to strive for more. Let me conclude this section by sharing with you a Bible verse that encourages increase: "Beloved, I wish above all things that thou mayest prosper and be in health, even as thy soul prospereth." ,3 John 1:2 (NKJV), "The thief does not come except to steal, and to kill, and to destroy. I have come that they may have life and that they may have it more abundantly." , John 10:10 (NKJV)

Level Up - Summary

"Whereas you do not know what will happen tomorrow. For what is your life? It is even a vapor that appears for a little time and then vanishes away.", James 4:14 (NKJV) I vividly remember my mother often quoting this Bible verse. It resonated with me as a child and even more so today in my adult life. As I grew older my desire and passion to achieve more grew. I'm no longer comfortable with a predictable or mundane life. I want more. I no longer want to settle for less than what God says I can have. So, within the timeframe of your life, why not attempt to go after more? Why not attempt to grab all of your heart's desires before leaving this earth. Please know that you're not going to always be able to do so in leaps and bounds. And that's ok. Take baby steps, or crawl if you must. But continue to move in the right direction. Be mindful to move forward as you attempt to take your life to the next level up.

Chapter 14
Plan,
Push,
Prayer

Plan Description

A plan is a strategic outline, step-by-step list of actions to take in sequential order in such a way that it leads to a desired outcome and or results in one accomplishing a goal. Having a plan for your life is a must. I can't stress enough the importance, and the positive impact a plan can have on your life. A friend once shared with me the following old cliché, "If you fail to plan, then your plan is to fail." For years I did not have a strategic plan for my life. I had goals that I wanted to accomplish, and I had even written down a to-do list on several occasions. I came to realize that writing down goals and randomly creating a to-do list was a good place to start, but without a strategic written plan, most of my goals remained out of reach, and my to-do list was often carried over to the next day.

The year was 2011, and it seemed like I was in one of the biggest fights of my life. That year I went through many stressful transitions: Breaking down, dismantling, packing, and moving from a home where I had lived for eight years. I funeralized my mother, and coped with the stress of my oldest son relocating, who moved over a thousand miles away from me. I also finalized my divorce while fighting for both my mental and physical health. In addition, I made great attempts to encourage and guide my adult children and grandchildren down a new life path which led them further away from a familiar place they once called home. It was a very stressful and challenging year. In order to survive, and not fall apart, I knew I needed a plan.

Plan - Roadblocks

Why is it that many individuals neglect writing out goals or creating plans for their life? There exists an array of reasons, but let me share with you some of my personal reasons as to why I had never written out a plan. First of all, I didn't know I needed to. I was ignorant of the fact that some Individuals routinely created and implemented life plans. I simply just didn't know that writing out a life plan possessed the ability to change and alter my life for the better. Secondly, I didn't know how to write a plan. I had no idea how to construct one. I recall some years ago attending a financial workshop. The main topic was on how to create a business plan. The facilitator also briefly spoke on the importance of creating life plans. She shared some of her personal goals and details as to how she created personal plans of her own. The seminar was very interesting. But although I was intrigued, I was not motivated enough to take immediate action. That leads me to my third roadblock which is procrastination.

Plan - How To

It wasn't until roughly 2011 that I took a serious look at my life and decided to strategically focus on creating a plan for it. I first had to address the busyness of my life. It was pertinent that I carve out some "think" time for myself. I literally had to stop, sit down, reflect, and think about which direction I wanted to go in life. So that is exactly what I did; I sat down and thought about my current life situation and the changes I wanted to see in my life. In order to change or transform your life, you will need a plan. The first thing I did was pray; I asked God to help me devise a plan to correct the many problems that were simultaneously occurring in my life. Then

I sat down on the edge of my bed with paper and pencil in hand. There were so many pressing issues that I wanted to address, but my main concern was my mother, her health and well-being. My mother had become ill, and she now needed 24-hour care. In bold letters, I wrote out my goal statement at the top of the paper; "how do I secure professional 24-hour care for my mother?" I immediately began to brainstorm, and to my surprise, it didn't take long to create a list. I had roughly written out eight steps to accomplish my plan. There were phone calls to make, doctors to visit, papers to fill out, people to meet, shopping to do, and hard and difficult conversations to be had. Attempt to write your plan out as detailed as possible. Avoid writing out vague goals. Your plan should have measurable goals. For example, if you want to lose weight, don't simply say, "I'm going to lose weight." Add details, for example, say, "I'm going to get up one hour early every morning and walk on my treadmill for thirty minutes before going to work." When you write out more defined goals it makes it much easier to measure your results.

Be specific about what you want to see occur in your life. You may want to lose weight, get a better job, get out of debt or build better relationships. Whatever that one thing is that you desire, create a plan to obtain it. First, get in a quiet place; then pray, reflect, meditate, or whatever it is that you do when attempting to block out the noise of the world. Focus on that one thing that you would like to see transpire within your life. Secondly, clearly and boldly write it out at the top of a piece of paper. Thirdly, directly underneath your targeted goal, write an expected completion date. It's important to create a sequential order of steps to follow. Once your to-do list is complete, it's imperative that you immediately take action. Work on the first item on your list. Procrastination can delay or even stop the process. It's helpful to draw a line through each completed action. You can also place a checkmark, asterisk or any markings of your choice to highlight and indicate that a step has been completed. Whenever I marked an item off my list I was encouraged by my progress. I would often write the current date and time next to each step completed. Lastly, celebrate each step that draws you closer to your goals. In addition, share your accomplishments with loved ones, and invite them to celebrate with you. Sharing your successes can help motivate you to tackle your next goal.

Plan - Summary

I have known people to write out their plans, fold the piece of paper, and put it away in a drawer, a file, or a folder for safekeeping. By doing so they hope that somehow their plans would jump off the page of the paper and somehow magically present themselves. That is not normally how it works. But honestly speaking, that's the belief of many individuals. I strongly suggest that once you write out your plan, do not put it in a drawer or tuck it away in a folder. It needs to be visible. Place your plan in a location where you can see it every day. The ability to visibly see my plan every day motivated me to continuously work toward my goals.

Prior to discovering how to write out a plan, my thoughts and emotions were all over the place. I was often frustrated, fearful, and fatigued. Sometimes life can be overwhelming and those were my exact sentiments during the onset of my divorce. There were days that I did not know if I was coming or going. Writing out a plan gave me stability, focus, and greater peace. The following Bible verse was very impactful, "And the Lord answered me, and said, write the vision, and make it plain upon tables, that he may run that read it.",

Habakkuk 2:2 (KJV) This scripture was the catalyst that motivated me to create plans for my life. For years I had always created a to-do list, but once I created a written plan it yielded greater results and a sense of accomplishment. When you do not have a plan for your life, then it creates greater opportunities for you to become part of someone else's plan.

Once I had my plan laid out on paper, I felt empowered and encouraged. This one simple act drastically changed my life, literally overnight. You may ask, how did my life suddenly change overnight? The moment I wrote my plan on paper, a wave of peace and relief washed over me. The pressure and the weight of the world which I had carried on my shoulders for months became much lighter. It was then at that moment, with my plan in hand, that I knew things were about to change for the better. Actually, reading it out loud changed my perspective. At that moment, I softly spoke under my breath, "I can do this, I can change my circumstances, and it is possible that I can live a better life." That very day, I set out to do exactly that. I immediately took steps toward accomplishing my first goal. Once that goal was accomplished, I wrote another one and repeated the process as needed. The first time I wrote a plan down on paper was in 2010. Because of that one act, the following century yielded for me an increase.

Push Description

Once you implement your plan, whatever it may be: to lose weight, start a business, or further your education, know that there will be challenges. Please know that the majority of the time you are going to run into obstacles that may seem insurmountable. At that exact moment, an opportunity will present itself. You will be given the opportunity to make a choice to either quit, give up, or push forward. Push is the act of applying force or pressure in an attempt to move something or someone. Push can also be expressed as one's willpower, or one's drive to accomplish something, especially when faced with obstacles. You can push both physically and mentally. For example, you can physically push someone to make them stumble or fall. You can also mentally push a negative thought from your memory by replacing it with the positive one.

Oftentimes when we set out to accomplish our goals, it's not often that they are handed to us on a silver platter. The odds are great that it will not be obtained effortlessly. Usually, anything worth going after is worth fighting for. With that being said, don't allow doubt, disappointments, or difficulties to distract, derail, or detour you from going after and achieving your goals. Have you ever been let down, disappointed, and felt like quitting, throwing in the towel, and giving up? On numerous occasions, I definitely felt like giving up. Each time I stop pushing or stop trying, I experience some level of regret, dissatisfaction, and or remorse. On the other hand, each time I persevered in spite of tragedy and hardship, I felt good about my decision to do so. The decision to persevere was definitely rewarding, but it's not always easy to do.

Push - Roadblocks

Most often, when you go after your goals and the things you desire, life happens, such as disappointments, setbacks, delays, or just small bumps in the road. When you're faced with difficult situations, do you allow negative thinking to overtake you or do you dig your heels in, brace yourself and push in an attempt to move the barriers that lay before you. When you find yourself faced with these circumstances, you have two choices: push forward or pull back. You may be surprised that many of us pull back. Why is it that many of us don't push back or push forward when something difficult or challenging occurs in our life? Was it too painful? Maybe you were afraid? Fear, fatigue, doubt, and procrastination were a few of my personal roadblocks. Each prevented me from putting my best foot forward and persevering when faced with challenges.

Fear

Again, fear was one of my biggest obstacles. Many years ago, I recall when some unexpected tragedy would occur, I immediately became fearful. I thought about all the negative aspects of the situation. I often thought about all the possible negative outcomes and all the ways the situation could just spiral out of control. I used to allow toxic thoughts to wash over me which would create more fear. It was very seldom that I would think of or focus on positive outcomes.

Fatigue

Have you ever felt tired, exhausted, or drained? Has there ever been a time in your life when you were neither physically nor mentally able to exert any form of energy, let alone the ability to push? Working and raising children often require parents to possess a large amount of energy. That's why it's highly recommended that you have your children while you are young; at least, that's what my mother would often suggest. I discovered that she was correct. I recall working a full-time job, fighting traffic to get home, picking up kids from after-school programs, cooking dinner, helping with homework, and trying to sum up enough energy at the end of the day to put on my pajamas and fall into bed. Those days would often seem endless.

It seemed abortive to try to come up with creative ways to fight off weariness from both bodily and mentally exertion.

Doubt

Then there was doubt. Sometimes while in despair I would often think that my current situation was hopeless. Have you ever second-guessed yourself or third, fourth, or fifth-guessed yourself? There were times I would come up with solutions but then immediately second guess myself which would often increase my doubt. I would then immediately think and often speak out loud, "what the heck? There's nothing I can do that would change the situation." When you are consumed with doubt you very seldom possess the ability to put forth an effort.

Procrastination

There were some broken areas in my life that I had intentionally avoided. My decision of continuous avoidance only prolonged the problem, causing me to stay within a negative situation and or within negative relationships. For whatever reason, I just didn't want to deal with certain issues or stressful situations. It could've been that I just didn't want to face facts. But whatever the reason, confronting and addressing problems and issues in my life were often put on hold. Unfortunately ignoring and putting things off often caused massive delays in my plans.

Push - How to

Over the years I have tried several ways to work through my doubts, fears, and procrastination. It's only been within the past few years that I have discovered one of the most effective ways to eliminate them all. And that is to take immediate action. I discovered that procrastination often increased my doubts which eventually led to massive fear. Now I must admit that I still find myself fighting to overcome procrastination, but not as frequently as I once did. It took a lot of practice. Movement is the solution, even if its baby steps.

Fear

Several years ago, someone once told me, "When you are afraid, do it afraid." This one small piece of advice literally changed the course of my life for the better. When I became fearful of doing something, I literally did it afraid, and the results were astounding. Whenever I had to do something and fear arose, I immediately forced myself to act. I did the one thing that I was afraid to do. And the more I responded this way I noticed fear started to subside and eventually dissipate. Courage is like a muscle; the more it is expressed, the more you become fearless. Courageous individuals often possess a certain level of fear, but they will not allow fear to stop them. As I mentioned in an earlier section, fear will dissipate and often disappear when you act and attempt to do that one thing you are afraid to do. The following is a Bible verse that always motivates me to push past fear: "For God hath not given us the spirit of fear; but of power, and of love, and of a sound mind." ,2 Timothy 1:7 (KJV)

Fatigue

Have you ever felt loaded down with the pressures of life? Your daily responsibilities can become overwhelmingly exhausting. When life becomes draining and saps most of your energy, and you feel extreme fatigue, then take a moment. The following are a list of ideas to help relieve weariness and fatigue: take a deep breath and then slowly breathe out, sit down, take your shoes off and put your feet up, take a power nap, take a day off from work, take a walk in the park, call a good friend, or recite positive affirmations. These are just a few of the things I like to do when I have become overwhelmed or have overextended myself. But please do whatever you need to do to recenter yourself, to build your energy and to get you back on track. The main idea here is to pause, not to park before you continue to push.

Doubt

When attempting to minimize or eliminate doubt it's imperative to try not to rehearse past failures. Actually, do the opposite; remember and reminisce about your past accomplishments and achievements. Remember your past victories, events, and things that brought you joy and peace. Reminisce on the last thing you did that made you feel good about yourself. It's important not to compare your accomplishments with others when experiencing self-doubt. Let me end this section with a befitting Bible verse: "I can do all things through Christ who strengthens me." , Philippians 4:13 (NKJV)

Procrastination

Initially eliminating procrastination was extremely difficult for me. I had a bad habit of putting things off. I simply didn't want to address or deal with some problems or issues that may have arisen. There were times when I would ignore the problem for a duration of time only to discover that it had fixed itself. Now I know ignoring and putting things off is not the best way to deal with a dilemma. Nevertheless, I did that for quite some time until I discovered a better approach. Usually, on Monday morning, I would often create a to-do list such as: cleaning out the garage, doing yard work, doing the laundry, paying bills and cleaning my car out before taking it to the car wash. By the time Friday rolled around I might have completed only one of my tasks. In order to avoid compounded frustration and being totally disappointed with myself I had decided to partially address everything on my list. For example, instead of cleaning out the entire garage or cleaning out my entire car, I would partially clean it out each day of the week. I would often spend 10 to 20 minutes each day on each task until it was completed. Although I was unable to invest an hour or more to complete a task, I still had a sense of accomplishment. Over time I was able to increase the amount of time I spent on each task, which eventually helped me eliminate procrastination in several areas of my life.

Push - Summary

I remember as a child lying in the bed or just sitting around the house and my mom would unexpectedly ask me to get up to do my chores or run an errand. I would often respond, with the utmost respect of course, "Mom, I don't feel like it." I vividly remember her responding as such, "Your feelings have nothing to do with it, now get up and do what I asked." My mother was trying to convey to me that there would be times in my life that I would need to act, and do some things regardless of how I felt. In doing so it creates opportunities and experiences that can lead to greater things. This was a valuable life lesson, and mom was absolutely correct.

I recall on several occasions thinking that I could neither physically nor mentally put forth an effort because I was tired, angry, lonely, or possibly exhibiting an array of other similar emotions. But yet, I was still able to push past these emotions in order to go to work. Why is it that we often push ourselves to go to a job but we won't push ourselves to go after our dreams? I want to encourage you to tap into that same secret place that lies deep within you. It's the same area where you find the strength to get up early in the morning and go to work when you don't feel like it. It's the same area you tap into when you go jogging on an early cold and windy autumn morning. It's that same reservoir that you tap into when you get out of bed at 12 am, 2 am, 4 am, and every two hours that follow in order to feed your newborn. Mothers often do so in spite of fatigue, weariness, and even postpartum depression. The point I'm trying to convey is that we have the ability to summon strength, tenacity, grit, and courage to push past obstacles in an attempt to reach our desires and goals. Lastly, I want to encourage you to make a commitment to push, to fight for your dreams, even if it's something as simple as fighting to resist the urge to hit the alarm clock, roll over, and put your head back under the cover and go back to sleep. No matter how minuscule, or monumental, move forward by exerting some form of force whether it be in leaps and bounds or baby steps.

Prayer - Description

Although prayer is mentioned last here among the twelve suggested help techniques, by far it is not the least important. Prayer was actually one of the first steps I implemented when I attempted to correct the many broken areas in my life. As a young child, I had always been taught to pray. Each night before I went to bed my mother taught me this simple prayer; "Now I lay me down to sleep, I pray the Lord my soul to keep, and if I die before I wake, I pray the Lord, my soul to take." At each meal, she taught me the following prayer; "God is good, God is great, let us thank him for our food, amen." These prayers may sound very familiar to some, but to others, it may not. This may be your first time hearing such a prayer, and it may actually seem foreign. Throughout the years I have discovered that prayer can have a tremendous effect on one's life. Many years ago, I remember my mother used to always tell me that prayer will change things. She was absolutely right. Whether a short brief prayer or an hour-plus long or elaborate prayer, it has the ability to change a person's life. Subconsciously I knew I was not living my best life for most of my marriage. I prayed, and I prayed all the time. Prayer is basically having a conversation, a one-on-one dialogue with God. Every morning upon awakening, before I went to sleep at night and even several times throughout the day, I took time to talk with God. Now I must admit that there was a time in my life that I did not pray on a regular basis. It took time to develop my daily prayer life. I'm truly grateful to even possess a prayer life considering there are several obstacles to prayer.

Prayer - Roadblocks

Kneeling down beside my bed with the palms of my hands pressed together, head bowed and praying to God before I jumped into bed and nestled myself between my sheet and my comforter had become a nightly routine as a child. I believe it was somewhere between middle school and starting high school that I began to fall out of the habit of kneeling down and praying. What could have caused me to no longer say my prayers each night? My bed hour had changed; could that have been the reason? By the end of high school and the beginning of my freshman year of college, I noticed that my nightly prayer routine had drastically changed. I asked myself why? I know why, I had become preoccupied with life, responsibilities, obligations, and the busyness of it all. Basically, I didn't have the time, so I thought or I simply wouldn't take the time to pray. Do you pray, and if not, why not? Could your reasons be found among the following list as to why individuals don't pray? The following are a few commonly known obstacles that prevent individuals from praying: time, doubt, or they just don't know how to. Many of us have busy schedules, and we simply just can't find the time to pray. Then there are those who simply don't pray because they don't think it's effective, in other words, they don't think prayer works. Lastly, many individuals believe prayer is effective but they simply don't know how to pray.

Prayer - How To Find Time

I remember a space and time in my life when I didn't pray very often. Sure, I said grace; I often quickly asked God to bless my food and thanked him for each meal before I ate. Sadly, that may have been the only time I had talked to God. We often find time to do everything but pray. It seems as if we all have busy schedules, things to do, and places to go, and many of us feel that there are not enough hours in a day. So, prayer is often pushed to the bottom of our to-do list. If you have become too busy to pray, then I want to encourage you to purposefully and strategically incorporate prayer into your daily activities. If you listen to music or watch television while working out on your treadmill, then cut the music off, or turn off the television and pray. You don't have to pray your entire workout; possibly pray during your warm-up or cool down. The ideal is to begin talking to God. I enjoy walking in the park. Being outdoors and surrounded by nature often encourages me to pray. I would also often take the opportunity to pray while driving in my car. Sometimes while driving I will turn on my favorite gospel song and meditate on the goodness of God. This would often lead to prayer. Some of our commutes are an hour plus long in one direction. Try it, turn your car radio off and start a dialogue with God. Following are other opportunities which can lead to prayer: while in the shower, cleaning your house, or even while sitting on the toilet. Instead of picking up a magazine, pick up a Bible. You're going to possibly be sitting there for a while so why not read your Bible and pray? I'm just saying, it's a start. The ideal is to look for and take opportunities to pray. Over time this can lead to increased prayer life.

Eliminate Doubt

Oftentimes people don't pray because they don't think it's effective. Maybe you used to pray, or maybe you once prayed and nothing happened. And now is it possible that you don't believe prayer is effective because God at one time didn't answer your prayers when or how you thought he should. Maybe you feel as if God disappointed you or let you down in some way, and inadvertently it has affected your prayer life. When people share with me their doubts and fears that God won't answer their prayers, I immediately ask them if God has ever done anything for them? I then remind them that if God has done anything for them, then he can do it again.

We must find ways to eliminate constant doubt. Over the years I have discovered some effective ways to do just that. First of all, I'm now more mindful of negative and depressing thoughts which often create doubt and despair. My mother would often tell me, "Don't let it wash over you." She was trying to encourage me to not allow anger, loneliness, doubt and other negative thoughts to consume me. She did not want me to continuously focus on such negative emotions. My mother very seldomly allowed negative thoughts to wash over her. She would often reflect and meditate on the goodness of God and how he miraculously answered her prayers. She also encouraged her children to maintain an attitude of gratitude. We often don't appreciate the small and simple things of life. Simple pleasures such as the ability to physically walk, access to food when you're hungry, a bed to lay your head, or somewhere to call home. If you have ever been denied these simple pleasures then have them returned to you, then most likely your appreciation and gratitude would have immediately and immensely increased. The ability to appreciate the smallest simplicities of life keeps me focused on God 's grace and mercy. The following are some Newfound habits which tremendously decreased my doubts: monitoring negative emotions, focusing on the good and positive things within my life, in addition to reciting daily affirmations. These new found habits have decreased my doubts.

Pray A Simple Prayer

Sometimes we don't pray because we simply don't know how to. I often tell people that prayer is basically a conversation with God. I used to believe that prayers should be long, drawn-out, and detailed. As a young child, I remember growing up in church and being fascinated by prayer. Each Sunday, I would intently listen to the pastor, the deacons, and the mothers' board as they led the church in prayer. They would often passionately and eloquently recite long elaborate prayers full of biblical scriptures, exhortations, and praise. I would often think, I wish I could pray with such fervor. With the passing of time, I learned how to implement different strategies and techniques of prayer into my own personal prayer life. The Bible offers several verses on how to pray. The following is just one of many of my favorite Bible verses in reference to prayer: "Be anxious for nothing, but in everything by prayer and supplication, with thanksgiving, let your requests be made known to God." , Philippians 4:6 (NKJV) A friend once hesitantly shared with me that they didn't know how to talk to God and that they simply just didn't know what to say. I shared with them an acronym for prayer, which I often share with individuals who have recently accepted Jesus Christ as their Savior. The following is an acronym for prayer and simple instructions on how to pray.

P- Praise

"Enter into His gates with thanksgiving, and into His courts with praise. Be thankful to Him, and bless His name." , Psalms 100:4 (NKJV) This Bible verse encourages us to start our prayers with praise and with a grateful heart. In other words, we should honor and thank God for who he is and for his many blessings. The following is a brief example of thanking and praising God when praying: "Father God, I thank you for all that you do. I thank you for keeping me, watching over me, and protecting me. For you are holy, and there is no other God above you. Hallelujah thank you Jesus."

R- Repent

"If we confess our sins, he is faithful and just to forgive us our sins and to cleanse us from all unrighteousness." ,1 John 1:9 (KJV). This Bible verse encourages us to admit guilt, wrongdoing, or any sinful acts which you may have committed and to know that God is faithful to forgive us. The following is an example of a prayer of repentance," Father God I messed up, I lied, I gossiped, I said something I should not have said, I intentionally hurt someone's feelings. Dear Lord, I stole; I took something that didn't belong to me. I was manipulative and deceptive. I admit that I have done wrong, I am sorry and I repent of all my sins."

A- Ask

"Ask and it will be given to you; seek and you will find; knock and the door will be opened to you.", Matthew 7:7 (KJV) "Do not be anxious about anything, but in every situation, by prayer and petition, with thanksgiving, present your requests to God.", Philippians 4:6 (NIV) God 's word not only encourages us to seek but also to ask God for our hearts' desires. Have you lately asked God for something, possibly for yourself or a loved one? "Father God, I pray that you keep me strong, healthy, and wealthy. I ask that you keep my children, my grandchildren, and many generations to come, and my friends and family strong, healthy, and wealthy. I ask you Lord to order our footsteps and keep our hearts and our minds toward you." That's a brief example of one of my own personal prayers as it relates to asking. Let me end this section with one additional Bible verse which encourages us to ask; "you have not because you ask not." , James 4:2 (KJV)

Y- Yield

"Call to me and I will answer you and tell you great and unsearchable things you do not know." Jeremiah 33:3 (NIV) This Bible verse not only reminds us that God encourages us to talk to him but it also reveals, that he wants to speak to us as well. Oftentimes we miss hearing the voice of God because we're not willing to listen. Have you ever been in a conversation with a loquacious individual? If so, then you would know how difficult it is to get a word in edgewise. Now, remember prayer is nothing but a conversation between you and God. But when we pray, we often do most of the talking. It's ironic that we would ask God for directions for our lives but we won't sit patiently and quietly and wait for his answer, directions, and or instructions.

E- Exultation

"The Lord is my strength and my shield; in him my heart trusts, and I am helped; my heart exults, and with my song, I give thanks to him." , Psalm 28:7 (ESV). In this Bible passage, I would like to focus on the word exult which can be interchanged with joy, and jubilation. The author of this Bible passage briefly explains how his heart exults, rejoices, and delights in the Lord as he sings and gives thanks to God for strength and protection. The writer of this verse encourages us to be cheerful over Gods' many blessings.

R- Repeat

Repeat the following areas of prayer as necessary or as needed: praise, repent, ask, yield, and exultation. You do not have to pray in this specific order or even address each of these areas when praying. For example, you might have a need to praise God throughout your entire prayer. You may find yourself sitting quietly for hours and listening to the voice of God. It's not necessary or required that we always pray a certain way each time. Sometimes a prayer could be just one sentence such as "I need you, Lord." Sometimes prayer can be one single word, such as help or Jesus. The Lord knows that there have been many times I have prayed such prayers. Please note that this acronym for prayer is a practical baseline for prayer.

Prayer- Summary

Now I will be the first one to admit that I am not an expert on prayer. But each day I purposefully make great attempts to pray. I can unequivocally and honestly say that this habit of prayer has improved my life and the lives of others surrounding me. Both my mother and my grandmother used to always tell me that prayer would change things. They were absolutely correct. As my prayer life developed, so did my faith. As my faith increased, so did my peace, my joy and my love for others. I want to encourage you that whatever you're seeking, whatever you're hoping for or desire, go to God in prayer. The Bible gives several examples of how to pray.

Let me close this section by sharing a well-known Bible verse that gives an excellent example of how we should pray.

"And when you pray, do not be like the hypocrites, for they love to pray standing in the synagogues and on the street corners to be seen by others. Truly I tell you, they have received their reward in full. But when you pray, go into your room, close the door and pray to your Father, who is unseen. Then your father, who sees what is done in secret, will reward you. And when you pray, do not keep on babbling like pagans, for they think they will be heard because of their many words. Do not be like them, for your father knows what you need before you ask him. This, then, is how you should pray: Our Father in heaven, hallowed be your name, your kingdom come, your will be done, on earth as it is in heaven. Give us today our daily bread. And forgive us our debts, as we also have forgiven our debtors. And lead us not into temptation, but deliver us from the evil one. For if you forgive other people when they sin against you, your heavenly Father will also forgive you. But if you do not forgive others their sins, your father will not forgive your sins." , Matthew 6:5-15 (NIV)

Reflections

Once I implemented many of these strategies into my life, it wielded surprising results. I have developed a closer walk with God, my relationships improved, my finances increased, and both my physical and mental health have improved. Now I must admit that results did not occur overnight, and some areas were more of a challenge to repair than others. Nevertheless, the effort and the wait were rewarding. Many of us often look for a quick fix to our problems. So often when you're giving advice, especially step-by-step advice as to how to improve, we often look for an instant turnaround. We often hear that we're living in a microwave society. That basically means we like to take a problem, put it in the microwave for a two or three-step program, and set it for one week, or one month, at high speed, hoping that everything will be made better, fixed, and complete. Truth be told, most likely you didn't break overnight, so most likely you will not repair, heal, or mend overnight. But please hear me and know that persistence and patience will bring about progress.

Chapter 15
Monitor,
Measure,
&
Maintain

Introduction

After taking steps to improve the broken areas of your life, I strongly and highly advise that you monitor and measure those same exact areas in an attempt to maintain improvement and or maintain complete repair. In doing so it creates the likelihood of long-lasting results. Within the following sections, I will share with you some examples of how I personally monitored, measured, and continue to maintain several areas of my life that were once broken.

Spiritual

For years, every Sunday, I had made great attempts to attend my local church services, especially during the Covid-19 pandemic. Although most of the churches had closed their doors during that time, I found other ways to hear the gospel. As the world was encouraged to stay at home, I faithfully viewed the services online or on television. I must admit that I was not always this determined or faithful when it came to hearing the word of God and going to church. I recall several years ago when my church attendance plummeted. It was a time when I developed many trepidations about the church. I had even decided to leave my local church. I left for an array of reasons; I didn't like the songs the choir sang, I didn't like the way the pastor preached, nor did I like how people sometimes looked at me or spoke to me. I know, I know it all seemed quite petty; but I was young and still spiritually growing.

But in my quest to find a new church home I must admit that I almost walked away from the church. Unfortunately, and unconsciously I had become comfortable sleeping late on Sunday mornings. It wasn't until one day that my youngest daughter, who was in grammar school at the time, asked me if we were going to church that particular Sunday. It was something in her voice and something in her eyes that caused me to feel sad at that moment. It also created an urgency within me to find a new church. I had always shared with my children the importance of attending and participating in worship services, studying the Bible, connecting, and fellowshipping with other Christians within the body of Christ. Long story short I did find a new church home and my children and I resumed attending church on a regular basis. After that incident, I became very mindful of my church attendance, Bible study and my prayer life.

Mental

Within the past five to seven years, I have been hearing more about the importance of mental health. I hate to admit it, but about thirty-plus years ago, I strongly believed that all therapists, psychiatrists, and counselors possessed the same goal. The goal was to overcharge their patients and pretend that they cared. Most of this train of thought stemmed from my childhood. Growing up as a child I never heard much mention about mental health. The idea of going and seeking professional mental health was not an option, nor even considered. It was never brought up or discussed and why should it? Because the majority of our family problems and issues were settled through discipline and or prayer. Now don't get me wrong we did sit down as a family and often discussed grievances and life concerns, but we would never seek professional counseling. That was simply unheard of.

As a child and even today, I would randomly hear people say the following: "Be strong, be a soldier and suck it up." These are terms often used to motivate others to endure hardships without complaining or expressing disappointment or other hurt feelings. Have you ever witnessed a parent attempting to stop their child from crying? Does this sound familiar; "Now, now, stop crying, don't be a crybaby; big girls, and big boys don't cry." That cannot be further from the truth because big girls and big boys do cry. Adults often cry, but parents sometimes fail to share this fact with their children. Our young boys are often encouraged to suck it up and be a man while in the midst of their childhood. They are often thrust into the roles of a leader, head of household, breadwinner, or a father before being given the opportunity to enjoy their adolescent years and early twenties. That in itself can create stress and mental anguish. In addition, they are often made to feel as if they can't share their feelings. The ability to freely express and share your feelings can be mentally liberating. I encourage you to monitor your thoughts; in other words, think about what you are thinking about. And lastly, if you have the desire to express those thoughts by all means do so.

Physical

Have you ever worked very hard to lose weight only to gain it all back, plus some? Well, I have, and even on more than one occasion. Now I must admit my weight still fluctuates roughly five to ten pounds more or less depending on the seasons. Years ago, I gained 30 pounds over a short period of time. I remember it like it was yesterday. The year was 1990 and I stepped on the scale and I immediately had to catch my breath. The scale blinked bright red numbers that read 187. I was in total disbelief. That was almost 190 pounds! That was my first thought. I weighed 200 pounds when I gave birth to my first son. In my third trimester of pregnancy, I was bloated, and retaining water, my ankles were swollen and I was big as a house. All I could think about was that I was practically ten pounds away from 200, which was my average pregnancy weight. I made a decision that day to lose the extra pounds.

It was not easy; it was a slow process. It took a year to lose the first ten pounds. In the following months I went on to lose an additional twenty pounds. I did a variety of things to help lose weight. I did some form of exercise every day in addition to eating more nutritious and healthy meals. The only determining factor which I believe helped me lose and maintain a healthy weight was my ability to monitor and measure my progression or the lack thereof. I initially bought a calendar and began to chart my daily exercise and my food intake. Reviewing my calendar each day tremendously helped me stay focused on my weight loss goals.

At the end of each week, I had a clear indication if I was on track or not. At the beginning of each week, I knew whether or not I had to increase my exercise and or decrease my food intake.

Financial

One of the best ways to monitor your finances is to create a budget. A budget should give you a clear outline of your assets and liabilities. Once you have an idea of your monthly income and your monthly debt, it can create an opportunity to increase your savings. Some research shows that the majority of households have less than $500 in savings. And why is this? It can be an array of reasons, such as the following: unemployment, overspending, large amounts of debt, no budget, or simply just lacking an understanding of finances. I recall a time when I had less than $500 in my savings account.

Truth be told, I had zero dollars saved; I was actually living paycheck to paycheck. That is a very difficult place to be for any given amount of time. I had over-extended myself and created a large amount of credit card debt. I felt trapped and overwhelmed. Late fees and high-interest rates created feelings of hopelessness. I often thought that I would never get out of debt. I had to force myself to take a close look at my finances which led me to reconstruct my budget. Over time I was able to eventually pay off a substantial amount of my credit card debt. Although it has now been several years, I still maintain a budget that I faithfully monitor on a regular basis. Routinely monitoring your finances has the potential to eliminate debt and increase your savings.

Relationship

A relationship can take on many forms. To avoid being elaborate, I will keep it simple by addressing couples who are married, individuals who are single and dating, and individuals who are simply platonic friends. Have you ever cared about someone who emotionally hurt you? Have you ever experienced a breakup or a divorce? Have you ever had a friend who stopped talking to you or who just stopped being a friend? I did. People develop different opinions, and sometimes separate and walk away from their marriage, partnerships, or friendships for a number of reasons. The following are some common reasons why people separate: finances, jealousy, loss of commonality, and betrayal. Today I'm more mindful of my relationships through a process I'd like to refer to as "checks and balances." It's a process in which I intentionally monitor my relationships. I am mindful to check, call and reach out to people to see how they're doing. I'm also mindful that there should be a balance within a marriage or friendship. Is your spouse or friends checking on you? Or are you doing most or all of the checking? When talking on the phone, do they routinely do most of the talking, and dismiss your concerns? If so, that can be a huge indicator that the relationship is not balanced and most likely, the two will separate and part ways. I'm also more observant of what's currently taking place in my friends' life. I literally or mentally take notes if my friends change jobs, lose a job, become pregnant, get married, get divorced, relocate, lose a loved one, become ill, or simply just have a bad day. These scenarios can have a negative or positive impact on an individual, which inadvertently can affect their relationship with you. Monitoring and routinely checking on your relationships may actually save it.

Timeline

In addition to monitoring the five areas recently discussed, it's also just as important to monitor an additional aspect of one's life, and that one pertinent aspect is "time". We often don't realize how precious time is. You can lose money and possibly get it back and you can lose your health and possibly get it back. But once you lose time you can never get it back. Have you ever heard someone say the following, "I just don't know where the time went?" After frequently saying this myself, I decided to search for my time. I wanted to know exactly where my time went when it slipped away or I lost track of it. I must admit that initially, it was very difficult to monitor my time. With persistence, I was able to do so. My efforts revealed some surprising results.

Every morning upon awakening, I would begin to list each of my activities and chart the amount of time it took to complete each task.

I immediately noticed that I was spending unnecessary extra hours on social media, watching television, talking on the phone, and randomly meeting with people. To rectify this situation, I decided to place many of my activities on what I like to call a "timeline." I would basically set a timer for any given activity of the day. For example, if I was working on my budget, I would often set the alarm to go off after 30-60 minutes. If I was exercising or even simply talking on the phone, I would still set a timer to end the conversation or my work out. Whatever I was doing when the timer went off, I would immediately stop. Over time I was able to see a clear and more accurate picture of how my time was spent. By doing so it allowed me to free up more of my time to invest elsewhere. Lastly, please do not allow people or circumstances to consume or waste your time. Time is such a precious commodity.

Reflection

I discovered some years ago that what gets measured gets accomplished. Basically, measurement is a quantity that can be expressed in numbers, size or the amount of something. Let me explain. I often measured my activities through the process of charting. Whenever I set a goal, I would write it in a notebook. In addition, I would also write out the steps I needed to take in order to reach that particular goal. Several times throughout the week I would open my notebook, review the steps and chart my progress or the lack thereof. For example, if I set a goal to lose weight and to work out every day, then I would mark in my notebook whether or not I worked out that day. Over time a pattern would emerge. At the end of each week, I knew exactly how many days I worked out and for how long. If I missed a day or two during the week then the following weeks, I would increase the intensity of my workout and or add an additional workout. The daily opportunities to review my notebook motivated me to stick with my weight loss regimen. This in turn yielded surprising and pleasant results. You might choose to use a single sheet of paper, a calendar, an index card, a poster board, sticky notes, or possibly an app. Whatever you choose to chart on make sure it's placed in a location where you are able to view it as much as possible throughout the day.

In summary, charting has the ability to increase your focus. My increased focus led to increased motivation, which increased my ability to reach some of my goals as scheduled and or even beforehand. Lastly, once you obtain your goal, you may choose to stop charting, but I want to encourage you to continue to monitor your success. For example, if your goal was to lose ten pounds and you successfully reached your goal, then why not continue to charge your weight. I suggest that you get on the scale maybe once or twice a week in an attempt to periodically monitor your weight. Continuing to monitor your weight will help eliminate unwanted surprises possibly in the form of extra pounds.

Chapter 16
Monitor
People

Introduction

There is an old and well-known cliché that states, "Birds of a feather flock together." Over the years, I have discovered this statement to be profoundly true. Individuals often associate with other like-minded individuals. You don't see eagles feeding with chickens, and within the same vein, you don't see millionaires living in poverty-stricken neighborhoods. Millionaires often are observed living in neighborhoods with other millionaires. The less fortunate are often observed living in neighborhoods with other individuals who are less fortunate. People tend to associate with individuals with similar values, backgrounds, incomes, and interests. Take a moment, and reflect on your five closest friends. Now compare their income, interest, aspirations, level of education, and accomplishments with yours.

Did you discover any similarities? More than often, our lives tend to mirror the life of our closest friends. Your closest relationships have the ability to alter and even change your beliefs, values, and behaviors which can negatively or positively transform your life. We tend to put people into groups and categories such as, besties, neighbors, co-workers, parishioners, and so on. Over the years I found myself placing people into the following groups: the good, the bad, the old, the new, and the few and true. Whichever way you tend to group people whom you associate with, just be mindful to monitor and evaluate those groups on a regular basis. Be mindful of the people you routinely associate with because they have the greatest influence, and the greater the influence, the greater the impact on one's character. With that being said, it will behoove you to monitor your closest relationships.

MILDRED "MICKEY" GIVENS

The Good

Do you have some family members and friends whom you may consider to have good character traits? Are they friendly, caring, and loving, and do they go out of their way to be helpful? Those are behaviors that are often exhibited by a good person. Sometimes we connect with that one really good friend who always seems to offer sound advice, at least most of the time. Take a moment and think about a person whom you may consider to be a good individual. Now ask yourself, have they ever given you bad advice? Good people can give bad advice. Although they may have all good intentions to offer their best advice, sometimes they may inadvertently offer bad advice. The bottom line is when you are offered advice always weigh your options,

I recall this speaker sharing his testimony about his mother; she appeared to be a sweet kind-hearted individual. She wasn't one who took risks, and she advised her son to do the same. The son had always respected and admired his mom, but this one particular day he refused and rejected her advice. The young man wanted to start a business. He knew there were some risks involved but nevertheless, he was willing to move forward. His mother, on the other hand, strongly advised against it. He launched his business and unexpectedly over a short period of time his business exponentially grew. It was an overnight success. He was elated that he didn't allow a good individual, whom he dearly loved to make him miss a lucrative opportunity.

The Bad

Do you know people whom you prefer not to be around nor invest time with them, and if so, why? Is it possible they're negative, toxic, or considered "bad" people? We want to be mindful of these individuals and the amount of time we spend with them. Sometimes we believe we can associate with pessimistic and gloomy individuals and it won't affect us, but it will, and it does. The following is one of my youngest daughter's favorite Bible verses: "Bad company corrupts good character." ,1 Corinthians 15:33 (CEB) I think it's highly important that we be mindful and careful about the company we keep. This is especially important for our younger generation, who are often more easily influenced by their peers. And I get it, sometimes it's extremely difficult to avoid unfriendly individuals. Oftentimes we work with them, go to church with them and many of us live with them. Young, old, and all of us in between need to practice how to disconnect, separate or limit our time with unpleasant individuals. I will be the first to admit that it's not always easy to do. So let me share one Bible verse relating to this topic, which tremendously helped me to stay focused and remain mindful of "bad" individuals. "Don't befriend angry people or associate with hot-tempered people, or you will learn to be like them and endanger your soul." , Proverb 22:25-25 (NLT)

The New

Have you recently met or been introduced to someone new? Who was it; were they a complete stranger, a new co-worker, or a blind date? It's all new and can be very exciting when meeting and getting to know someone for the first time. Several individuals we meet are initially pretentious or guarded. When we first meet someone, they rarely reveal their true character, especially within the business or dating arena. Within these types of settings people figuratively tend to wear masks. They often prefer to hide their identity and intentions. This is why it's imperative to monitor new relationships. I like to believe that people are genuinely honest, open and truthful, and trustworthy. Yes, many are, but it's also true that many are not. Sometimes people have alternative motives to meet and connect with you. They may want to meet and become acquainted with you for their personal gain, either financially or for physical reasons.

Granted, the majority of people you meet for the first time may not have an alternative motive. They may be sincere and honest. Nevertheless, new acquaintances have the potential to influence you either positively or negatively. Let me share an example within the workforce. I once knew a young lady who had been on her job for several years. She had always taken pride in her appearance. I recall when she shared her first day on her job. Many of her male co-workers had five o'clock shadows and wore unkempt clothes. The ladies in her office did not put much effort into combing their hair; as simple as that may seem to many. They also applied minimal or no makeup. Over time the entire office was influenced by this young lady. Throughout a span of months, several of the other employees began to take pride in their appearance. It had become apparent that the young lady had become a positive influence on her new co-workers. But the opposite could have occurred. For example, I have also observed individuals have a negative effect on their co-workers. I have witnessed a new employee transform from a dedicated, energetic, and hard-working individual to a lethargic, idle, and undependable individual. The new employee appeared to unconsciously take on the characteristics and behavior of their new co-workers.

The Old

The aged, the wise, big mama, pawpaw, grandpa, and or grandma; how do you refer to individuals who are roughly fifty-five years of age or older? These are the individuals who have roughly been on this earth for half a century or more. We tend to seek them out and ask for advice when we need guidance, wisdom, or direction in our life. Our older generation often possesses great insight and knowledge which they have accumulated throughout their many years. They often delight in sharing this information. As a child, I used to love to snuggle up next to my grandmother on the couch and just listen to her talk. Whichever way you refer to them, they are normally the group of individuals who are our senior citizens. It's a good idea to monitor and frequently visit these individuals. If only for the simple fact of gleaning from them, expressing love and appreciation and offering any form of assistance if requested or needed.

But I like to address another group of people who are considered old. For example, an old friend. Do you know someone whom you have known for several years, maybe a spouse, a neighbor, or a childhood friend? These are people you possibly have known for a long time. Most likely it took many years and much effort to build those long-term friendships. It also takes effort to maintain them. Initially, we often believe that close relationships will last forever; unfortunately, that's not true. Close friends tend to check on one another. But sometimes life can get hectic and we may not check on each other as often as we once did. When we fail to connect and check on one another, we often disconnect and separate. But for those individuals who make it a priority and a commitment to check on loved ones, friends and associates tend to maintain longer-lasting relationships. These relationships tend to fall into a category that I'd like to refer to as "few and true."

Few And True

Who are the few and true? These are individuals who have stood the test of time. They have been with you through good and bad times. They have supported and encouraged you. These are the individuals you can call late at night or early in the morning. They are dependable, reliable, and trustworthy. They are referred to by different names: bestie, true blue, ride or die, bosom buddy, pal, or simply a best friend. Do you have a close friend? Is there someone you can trust to share your secrets and private matters with? Maybe you know someone who you consider a confidant or bestie. A best friend is someone who cares, who is supportive, and who has your best interest at heart. I often hear married couples say that their spouse is their best friend, but later only to discover they are divorced. Best friends are a unique group of individuals. They possess a superpower which I like to refer to as staying power. Throughout life, people come and go, but truly good friends possess the ability to stick around for many years. These individuals usually stay connected throughout a lifetime. It's these individuals that need to be closely monitored, for the simple fact that they tend to have one of the greatest impacts on and in your life. Side note: if you live your entire life and get one best friend, then you did well.

What About You

Amongst all the people whom you need most to monitor is you. You truly need to monitor yourself. It's imperative to monitor your behavior and your total well-being. What does your life currently look like? To answer that question, you might have to take a long, hard look into your mirror. Go ahead, take a look first at your face, then your hair, and last your physical body. Have you changed much over the years? Have you gained or lost weight? Has your facial structure changed? Have you maintained body alignment or correct posture? I believe as we get older, it becomes a greater challenge to maintain a healthy weight.

Maintaining healthy thoughts can also become a challenge. When was the last time you took an inventory of your thoughts? We tend to be more aware of what people say to us than what we say to ourselves. Do you say things that uplift you, encourage, and motivate you? Maybe you are saying things to yourself that are demeaning and possibly destructive. For example, a pessimistic individual might say, "I'm stupid, I hate my body, I can't do anything right, or I will never get well." Many years ago, a man once told me that he would not live past the age of forty-five. I thought it was an odd thing to say, and it was hard for me to believe this man thought he would die before he reached the age of fifty. Surprisingly throughout my life, I have met and become aware of several individuals who also believed their life expectancy would be cut short. Just a couple of years ago a young man shared with me that he truly believed that he would not live past the age of thirty-two. Many of the men I spoke with believed in a short mortality because of family genetics, their social-economic status, or for the simple fact that someone told them so. Whether thirty-two, forty-five, before or after, or anywhere in between, regardless of the number, there are some individuals who believe that they are expected only to live up until a certain age. That's why it's so important to monitor your self-talk. Thinking and talking like this can actually shorten your life expectancy. On the other hand, it's actually possible to prolong one's life by monitoring what you say to yourself. Be mindful of saying more positive things to yourself, such as; "I'm beautiful, I'm handsome, I'm smart, I'm healthy, I'm strong, and I can do this." Saying such things has the potential and the ability to increase both physical and mental well-being. Let me share with you some of my favorite Bible verses which encourage me to monitor my behavior. "As a man thinks in his heart, so is he." (Proverbs 23:7) "Speak those things that are not as though they were." (Romans 4:17) "Death and life are in the power of the tongue: and they that love it shall eat the fruit thereof." (Proverb 19:21) In closing, please know and note that your thoughts and your words have the potential to increase or decrease the quality of your life.

My Five Closest Friends

It's often said that you are the direct reflection of the five closest people and or those individuals with whom you spend a great deal of your time with. I truly don't believe many of us realize the impact that people, specifically close friends, and family members, can have on our lives, both negatively and positively. Your five closest friends have the greatest impact on you. Oftentimes, people gravitate toward like-minded individuals. If your five closest friends are broke, you will most likely become the sixth broke person in the group. It has been said that you will roughly earn the same income as your five closest friends which can range between $1,000 and

$3,000 If your friends smoke, over time it's highly probable that you would pick up the habit of smoking. It's very likely that you will become a smoker also. If your five closest friends are overweight, research shows that most likely you will become overweight. On the other hand, if your friends are healthy, energetic, friendly, and financially secure then most likely, your life will resemble that of your friends. This transformation can occur gradually and unconsciously or intentionally. Let me end this section with two Bible verses that very much relate to this section: "Whoever walks with the wise becomes wise, but the companion of fools will suffer harm." (Proverbs 13:20), and "Don't befriend evil people or you will become like them and even endanger your soul." (Proverbs 22:24)

Slippery Places

My youngest daughter often says people tend to slip in slippery places. It so uniquely describes the effect broken people can have on others. Have you ever met an individual who possessed the opposite values of yourself? But overtime you surprisingly found yourself behaving in a similar fashion. Is it possible that you found yourself mimicking values that you possibly once loathed? Influence can be very subtle. The following is a story someone once shared and it tremendously resonated with me. It's an excellent example of subtle influence.

A pregnant dog ran into the street and was hit by a car. The dog lived, but both her back legs were broken. Although she was no longer able to sturdily walk on all four legs, she was still able to move about freely. She would use the strength in her front legs to drag her hips and hind legs to move throughout the house. The dog later gave birth to a litter of six puppies. The owner noticed that as the puppies grew, they began to drag their back legs. The owner immediately assumed that the puppies were somehow injured when the mother was hit by a car. Without hesitation, the owner took the puppies to a vet. After a thorough physical, the veterinarian deemed all the puppies in good health. He concluded that the puppies were mimicking their mother. Unfortunately, if the puppies continued to drag their legs, they would lose muscle and cause their back legs to atrophy. Over time, they can lose their ability to use their back legs. Who are you mimicking? Metaphorically have you developed a limp or are you dragging your legs because you're mimicking others who do?

Reflection

Good or bad, old or new, best friends or you; whichever category people may fall into, it's imperative that we monitor the people with whom we most often associate with. Good people have been known to do bad things, and bad people sometimes do good things. Lovers often become haters. Sometimes best friends walk away, severing a bond that should have lasted a lifetime. Have you ever met the love of your life, someone whom you considered your soulmate? Astonishingly, did they become bitter, resentful, or even malicious? It's possible that one's nemesis and arch enemy can become a reliable and trustworthy ally. In short, in any given time and space, people have the ability to change from good to bad and vice versa. It can be overtly obvious or unnoticeably subtle. You may wonder how you would monitor a relationship? Basically, be observant and more mindful of friends and associates. Be especially observant of milestones that may occur in their lives. For example, closely monitor birthdays, weddings, a divorce, a loss of a loved one, the birth of a child, job change, relocating, or a persistent illness. Change has the ability to mentally and or physically affect an individual in such a way that his or her outlook on life can drastically change. This can profoundly affect the people with whom they associate with. Lastly and just as important, be watchful and monitor that individual in your mirror.

Chapter 17
I.G.S

Introduction

After the implementation of the twelve help strategies, and techniques introduced in chapters 11 through 14, I noticed both subtle and drastic changes in my life. Although initially some of the strategies were more of a challenge to implement than others, nevertheless, each of the twelve techniques proved to have drastic results. I noticed several changes in my life along with different emotions and feelings. I was happier, more at peace, content, and satisfied as I noticed many of the broken areas in my life were being identified, addressed, fixed, or in the process of repair. Over time I noticed some of the areas within the twelve help strategies had longer-lasting results than others. And you might experience similar results. Wait a minute Mickey, are you saying these techniques are not long-lasting? The answer is yes and no; it can vary from person to person. But please know that every person can experience lasting results. In order to increase your possibility of lasting results you might want to investigate and consider rebuilding your Innate guidance system (I.G.S)

Innate Guidance System

What is an innate guidance system? It's a specialized mechanical device designed to control movement, speed, and other functions relating to the operations of planes, ships, missiles, satellites, and other such machinery. A plane can veer off course for several reasons, possibly due to a storm, heavy winds, heavy rain, or possibly mechanical failure. When this occurs, the plane's innate guidance system has the ability to adjust and control thrusters, flaps, wheels, and even the engine. The plane's I.G.S system has the ability to get the plane back on course and return it to its original flight path. It's similar to putting a plane on autopilot.

The same holds true for you and me. We also have an innate guidance system. Of course, it's not a mechanical device like the one Tony Starks possessed. Tony Starks is one of the main characters in a very popular movie entitled "<u>The Avengers</u>." He surgically implanted an I.G.S system into his chest. The device, along with a specialized suit gave him the ability to fly, and whenever he went off course the device was able to course-correct his flight path. Our innate guidance system was designed to also keep us on course. If we detour from our routine, habits, or our normalcy, then our I.G.S system has the ability to control one's behavior, speech, and movement in such a way that it can redirect an individual back to their original life path. Your innate guidance system (I.G.S) can best be described as your character, your personality, or basically your inner core. It's that one thing that makes you who you are. Some people may refer to it as habits, a program, or a paradigm. From the day we were born, we were programmed to act, speak, and behave a certain way. Our environment has the ability to shape and influence our behaviors to such a degree that in some instances we are unable to change or deviate from our norms even when we have a desire to do so. Our innate guidance system will often resist change. Although the ability to change can be difficult, it's not impossible. In the remaining sections of this chapter, I would like to discuss and share with you how I worked on and even continue to work on changing my I.G.S within each of the following five basic areas of life: spiritual, mental, physical, financial, and relational.

Spiritual

I vividly remember that day, it was a Sunday morning, and I sat nervously in the middle section of the pew. I fondly remember the church I attended as a child. It was a small storefront church; it was quaint but warm and welcoming. As the pastor gave the invitation to salvation, I knew that the moment and the time had come. I actually had made up my mind before I left the house. Earlier that Sunday morning, I told myself that I was going to join the church and give my life to Christ. It was near the end of his sermon, and as ritualistically, my pastor turned his head toward the choir and nodded. The organist immediately began to play softly. My pastor then closed his thick, noticeably worn bible, firmly gripped the lectern with his left hand, as he pulled himself forward and simultaneously extended his right hand toward the parishioners. He gave the invitation for salvation and asked, "Whosoever will?" as the choir sang, "Come to Jesus." I knew the invitation roughly lasted seven to twelve minutes, so I immediately stood up. I said excuse me each time I stepped over each parishioner's feet and gently pushed past their knees as I made my way to the end of the pew which was often positioned close to the pew directly in front of it which made it difficult to walk between.

At that moment, I possessed indescribable emotions as I nervously walked to the front of the church. It was so long ago; I was only seventeen. As I approached the pulpit, my pastor extended both his hands as he walked out to meet me. There, in front of the entire church, in front of my family and friends, I accepted Jesus Christ as my Lord and Savior as the pastor led me in the sinners' prayer. That precious moment was life-changing. Although it took place many years ago, I can still recall that exact moment as if it occurred

MILDRED "MICKEY" GIVENS

yesterday. From that day on, and moving forward, I began attending church on a regular basis and studying my Bible. I had developed such a love and a desire to know more about Jesus. I told everyone I knew about the love of Christ. I told anyone and everyone that would listen to how Christ saved me and how he can save them. I often shared the love of Christ with friends, family members, even strangers that I met on the street. I was "on fire for the Lord." As a child, this was a term I often heard spoken amongst adults as they referred to someone who loved the Lord and wasn't ashamed to share their faith; that accurately described me, so yes, 'I was on fire for the Lord." Over time I went from a roaring, blazing campfire, to what resembled a small flame which is often found at the head of a match after being struck. It had become obvious that I was no longer ministering and sharing my faith as often as I once did. I had fallen back into some old habits. I no longer read my Bible every day, and my church attendance had drastically plummeted. I was greatly concerned that I had started to drift away from the church. I still very much loved the Lord and had a desire to walk with him, but nevertheless, I found myself focused and pulled in other directions.

Does this sound familiar? Have you ever experienced a similar situation within your spiritual walk with Christ? Have you ever had a great passion or a strong desire to grow spiritually? Have you ever wanted a closer walk with God? Over time and for whatever reason, did you lose your passion, and if so, why? I truly believe the dramatic decline in my passion for walking with the Lord had a great deal to do with my initial spiritual innate guidance system. Why was it that I was no longer excited about sharing my faith, reading scripture, and even going to church? Why did my behavior no longer reveal or reflect the passion that I developed within my new walk with Christ? Why was my newfound faith shaken? There is your keyword, "newfound." It was new, it was different, my life had changed, and I had changed. It was the initial start of creating a new spiritual innate guidance system. Change has the potential to create the building blocks of a new innate guidance system. Prior to my newfound love for Christ, I was your average teenager, hanging out with friends, going to parties, playing sports, extra school curriculum, and dealing with peer pressure. I was basically dealing with everyday life pressures of a young teenage girl. My mother and grandmother had always taught me to love God and be respectful and kind. Like anything and everything else in my life, that took practice. That actually took not only practice but focus. And I must admit that back then, my focus had shifted from going to church and studying my Bible to the busyness of being a teenager. Fortunately, my mother was a constant example of a godly woman. I would often observe her praying, reading her Bible, and effortlessly offering care, support, and words of wisdom. It was my mother's continuous love and patience that encouraged and allowed me to shift my focus back to the church and to God. It was a slow process, but over time I returned to the church and resumed habits that increased my faith and my love of God.

Mental

I remember growing up as a very small child and watching both my father and my mother work very hard to provide for their family. For years I observed my family's household income fluctuate. There would be times of plenty, times where we would barely get by and there were times when we would have to go without. I so vividly remember those days of living in lack and not being able to purchase the necessities of life. There were times when we had very little money, a small amount of food, no electricity to light the house nor gas to heat the house.

Sidenote:

I remember one Thanksgiving Day when we didn't have gas. Money was short that month, and we couldn't afford to pay the gas bill, so the gas company cut our gas off. I remember laying in the bed thinking, "What's the point of getting up? There's no gas, so there's no way we can cook Thanksgiving food." I remember feeling very frustrated and angry. I laid there wrestled with thoughts of if I was going to get out of bed that morning or not. I don't recall what time it was but I remember hearing a knock at my bedroom door and simultaneously hearing my mother's voice on the other side of the door. My mother's voice was clear and distinctive as she energetically said, "Y'all come on and get ready to eat." I immediately became confused. But as I made my way into the kitchen, I immediately became elated. The table was set! In the middle of the table was a turkey with all the trimmings. My mother had cooked a turkey, sweet potatoes, turnip greens mac & cheese, hot water cornbread, and dessert all on a hot plate, two hot plates to be exact.

My mother was resourceful, and thrifty and she knew how to stretch a dollar. These were all good attributes to possess, especially when your finances were inadequate. Ironically if money was scarce or not my mother would often continue to shop for discounted items. Although my mother's resources and finances had increased over the years, she somewhat maintained a scarcity mindset. For years I had watched my mother shop for discounted food, clothes, and household items. Mom had fallen into a habit of purchasing the lower ticketed price items even when she could afford the regular or higher-priced items. I don't believe mom ever realized that she had developed a mindset of mediocracy. Overtime I observed my mother purchase quality and higher-priced items, but it was often done with careful thought and consideration. I must admit that some years back, and with the help of my youngest daughter, I discovered that I too had a similar mindset. Sometimes we unknowingly develop a poverty mindset; we believe and act as if we deserve less. We often avoid greater and the finer things of life even when we're in a position to possess those things. With patience and persistence, my daughter helped me identify some major broken mindsets. She was able to assist me by pointing out some of my own poverty mindsets which developed from my childhood

Physical

I know a young lady who had struggled with her weight for many years. She had tried dieting, exercise, and a number of weight loss programs but to no avail. She stopped trying; but as fate would have it, out of the blue, she decided to try again. Although she didn't exercise much, she did cut back on her calories which yielded tremendous results. This time the weight came off and stayed off for months. But unfortunately, after less than a year, she started to overeat, and the extra pounds returned. Like millions of other overweight individuals, she was disappointed and frustrated. Why is it that many can lose weight only to gain it all back within a short period of time? I know there are several reasons as to why individuals find it difficult to lose weight such as, lack of motivation, poor eating habits, medical reasons, and the list goes on. But your innate guidance system can also be one of the culprits. It was both eye-opening and disheartening when I discovered that I could actually be programmed to be overweight. I also have challenges with maintaining a healthy weight. I would lose the weight, then gain it back in a short period of time. It wasn't until the extra pounds affected my health and my well-being. It had become imperative that I get the extra weight off and keep it off, but how? If I was programmed to be overweight, how in the world would I be able to lose the weight and keep it off? I had to be reprogrammed; I had to simply change my innate guidance system. But there is nothing simple or easy about changing one's IGS. I had to eliminate some old habits and create some new ones. With increased motivation and tenacity and of course a plan, I was able to sparingly eat sweets. I was also able to reach a point where I eliminated some other unhealthy foods from my diet. I also did some form of physical exercise on a daily basis. These new habits led to a weight loss of thirty pounds.

Financial

I once heard a story about an old lady who was in her late eighties and unexpectedly died. After she passed away, her family discovered thousands of dollars stuffed between her mattress. On the other hand, I have heard stories about senior citizens who have died penniless. Unfortunately, their family members had to beg and borrow money just to bury them. Both these individuals died and left this earth without truly knowing how to manage money. One person was programmed to stuff money between her mattress, the second individual was possibly programmed to overspend. I recall a time when I was programmed to overspend. I didn't know how to balance my checkbook, create a budget, or efficiently manage money. I remember some years ago working a part-time job and working within a meager budget. I would often become frustrated because I wasn't able to purchase some of the things I wanted. I vividly remember my mother responding in her soft and teachable voice, "Now Mickey, it's not going to always be like this, there will come a time when you will be able to buy the things you want." It was the way she said it and that look in her eyes that made me always believe her. My mother worked very hard. She was programmed to work every day and manage an average income for most of her life. I was set on that same trajectory until I made a decision to seek out ways to increase my income.

I took a detour and signed up for financial seminars and classes which explained how to manage and increase my money. I immediately implemented the strategies I had learned. Over time I was able to eliminate a substantial amount of debt but my income and my savings had not changed very much. This was disheartening and caused me to slowly slip back into my old spending habits. Sometimes when things do not happen as quickly as we would like them to, we sometimes give up and throw in the towel. Once I stopped attending the classes I quickly found myself exhibiting old spending habits which eventually led to increased debt. I had fallen back into a spending pattern of familiarity. I strongly believe this occurred because of the way I was wired; it was the way in which I was programmed to spend money. Fortunately, with the support and encouragement of close friends and some family members, I was once again motivated to invest in my financial future. I signed up and attended seminars, webinars, and local meet-up small groups to discuss how to improve one's finances. I was able to meet and connect with individuals who checked on me and held me accountable for my financial goals. It was all very new and interesting. My views about money have now drastically changed. I no longer focus on living paycheck to paycheck. I no longer focus nor desire to settle for average income or just getting by. I want financial freedom!

Relationship

Have you ever broken up with someone and told yourself that you were done, you were through with them and added that you never wanted to see that person ever again? But to your surprise and your dismay, did you find yourself once again wrapped in their arms and rolling between the sheets? And after all was said and done you wanted to kick yourself. You might have asked yourself for the one-hundredth time, "What was I thinking, and how did I end up in bed with them?" Maybe you have several reasons as to why but please allow me to add another. I believe we end up in bed with our ex or past lovers because we are wired to do so. You might ask, "What does that even mean?" In other words, we are often programmed to gravitate toward the familiar. Shortly after my divorce, I would often find myself out running errands or leaving work and then driving in the direction of my once marital home. That was my routine for many years and it had become a habit. I had become programmed to drive directly to that house for roughly eight years.

Although the ink had long dried on the divorce papers, my marital innate guidance system was still fully intact. It was still up and running and functioning perfectly as if I was married. Several months after my divorce, my I.G.S system continued to pull me in the direction of my old home. And if the truth is told, if I find myself today in the west suburban area of Chicago, I can sometimes still feel a slight inner tug to go in the direction of my old neighborhood. Despite the fact that it had been months since I moved out of that house, I was still programmed to gravitate toward that place I once called home. Now since we're telling the truth, and being honest, let me say this; although I was divorced, I was still programmed; like that house, to gravitate toward this man; my ex-husband. Now I did not stalk him, search through his social media page nor did I sit outside his place of employment or his residency. I did nothing of the sort. But I can now better understand why some people who are recently divorced or separated can do such things. I believe they do so because they're programmed; they are wired to be with that individual. And as they mentally and emotionally work through the break up they sometimes find themselves missing the familiar and longing to return, even if that familiar is toxic. I didn't physically gravitate toward him but I did mentally. Initially, if I heard a song on the radio that reminded me of him, I would immediately change the station or turn the radio off. If someone mentioned him or brought his name up in a conversation, I would politely ask them to change the conversation. Practicing these simple behaviors while continuing to focus on my goals, and my physical and mental health greatly assisted me in rewiring old marital innate guidance systems.

Let me close this section by sharing a brief life experience of a dear friend. I met her many years ago when she was in her late twenties. I vividly remember her sharing the accounts of the events leading up to her devastating breakup with her longtime boyfriend. He was a confused, broken, and abusive young man. Unexpectedly and abruptly, he ended the relationship. He broke up with her and walked away and never looked back. Although he was a functional alcoholic, used drugs, and was unable to secure a steady job, she desired to be with him. After several months she did find the strength to move on. Unfortunately, she continued to date men who possessed similar character traits to her once abusive boyfriend. She asked me one day why she continues to get involved with toxic and abusive men? Could it be that she is programmed to do so? Could it be that her innate guidance system pulls her in the direction of abusive and castigating men?

Reflection

In summary, an innate guidance system is a set of habits repeated over a period of time. Within time and space, these habits will influence, impact and even control your behavior. And this can all transpire unbeknownst to you. Many of us are unaware that we are similar to a computer. We often purposefully download desired programs and software into our computers and many other electronic devices. I often download some of my favorite apps onto my phone and not give them a second thought. We also pay little attention to the software, the programs that continue to be downloaded to us on a regular basis. We have been influenced and programmed to think, react, behave, feel and speak a certain way. We have all been programmed since the day we were born. Some researchers believe that the program can even begin before birth.

Now how do you dismantle and break down an IGS system? Is it possible to replace it with another system? Yes, it is. Before we begin to break down old innate guidance systems, let's first address how they're built and how they initially came to be. Again, IGS systems are usually built into planes, ships, and other such machinery. These systems are usually programmed by scientists and individuals possessing specialized technical skills. The innate guidance system can also be found within the animal kingdom which is often referred to as instinct. When it comes to you and me, our innate guidance system is quite different. Our experiences, what, and who we are exposed to on a daily basis will affect our behaviors. When a certain behavior is repeated over a period of time, it becomes a habit, and our habits are the building blocks of our innate guidance system. In order to change our innate guidance system, we have to develop new building blocks. In other words, we have to create new habits. Creating new habits often requires that we become deliberate and determined. Initially, when I start a new habit, I write it down. I immediately take out a sheet of paper and write down the habit I want to create. I also chart how often the desired behavior is exhibited. By doing so I become more focused and intentional in creating the new behavior. Over time your resolve will create new innate guidance systems.

Before I end this section, I must share with you a conversation that I had with my granddaughter which is very befitting as it perfectly relates to the subject matter. Without warning my granddaughter, Cydnee boldly and inquisitively asked me if divorce is in our genes? I immediately and unequivocally responded no. She thought that because I was divorced and her mother was in the process of a divorce, she would get married and later get divorced. I reassured her that just because my marriage and her mother's marriage did not work out, will not predestine her to get a divorce. I encouraged her that she can grow up, and get married to a man who will love, honor, respect, and cherish her. I made it perfectly clear that she and her future husband can raise children, live in a beautiful home, have a career, and happily remain married for the duration of their life. But what I did not tell her is that although divorce per se is not within one's genes but nevertheless, it has the ability to be downloaded and programmed within an individual's subconscious. Now that's another story and more research for another time. "Whatever Natalie!" That's an inside joke. With all jokes aside, I strongly believe that it's imperative that we monitor our innate guidance systems. By doing so we can avoid many of the pitfalls and challenges which we often face in relationships and marriages. Don't be discouraged when attempting to create and monitor new habits. Just know that it's a process, and that persistence and patience will lead to progress

Chapter 18
All
In

Introduction

A couple of main points I would like to stress and would love for you to take away from this book are simple; processes, persistence, and patience. Please know that there's a process to better and the first step is to identify and become aware of your brokenness. Once you target the broken areas in your life, then make a commitment to take the necessary steps to repair them. We often don't break overnight, so most likely we will not repair overnight. In order to be truly committed, I suggest that you be "all in." I came up with an acronym for "all in" as a way to help you easily remember and reflect on some key points mentioned throughout the book. The acronym for "All In" is Ask, Listen, Look, Investigate, and Nothing.

Throughout my personal journey of repair, I constantly measured my progress or the lack thereof. Over time, and throughout the entire process, I discovered and came to realize that what gets measured, gets accomplished. I would either weekly, monthly, quarterly or annually chart and monitor my plan of action. This strategy helped me maintain my focus. Most of the areas that I attempted to improve were monitored on a monthly basis. Each month I asked myself specific questions, I listened intently, looked closely, investigated strategically, and purposefully did nothing. These daily behaviors helped me tremendously as I attempted to stay committed to improving and repairing the broken areas of my life.

Ask

Initially, it may be difficult to identify broken areas in your life. What helped me, and what I strongly believe can also help you is to first ask yourself some questions. Questions that will cause you to think and reflect on your current life and hopefully motivate you to investigate your current comfort zones. The following are a few of the questions that I asked myself, which helped expose some broken areas in my life. Ask yourself questions pertaining to your present status in life. Furthermore, ask yourself questions pertaining to your future. Honestly ask yourself some of the following and similar questions:

* "I'm I living my best life?"

* "What is my purpose in life?"

* "Do I want to spend the rest of my life being mistreated, disrespected, and or abused?"

* "Can I honestly say that I am happy?"

* "Have I been a good friend?"

* "Is it possible to have greater friendships, greater wealth, and greater health?"

* "Is this how I initially envisioned my life?"

* "Have I settled for less?"

* "Do I need a plan for my life?"

* "Where do I see myself next year or the next five or ten years?"

Asking such questions can start constructive dialogue within yourself and or with others. Asking certain questions can be the catalyst to the answers that can change your life.

Listen

Within my own personal repair process, I discovered that I had to be willing to listen, despite the fact that it was extremely difficult to do at times. I need to encourage you to listen to people and pay close attention to what people are saying to you or about you. Listen to both friends and foes. Listen to those individuals whom you possibly have been ignoring. Who have you been ignoring lately, putting off, or shunning? Do you avoid picking up the phone when a certain individual calls? Is it possible that you have been ignoring your parents, your siblings, your spouse, or a close friend? Is it possible that you have been ignoring them because you don't want to hear what you know to be sound advice? Could it be the advice of your parents encouraging you to eat better, get your rest, lose some weight, save your money, go back to school, go to the doctor, and get that pain checked out? Sometimes it can be difficult and painful to hear the truth and facts.

Not only listen to those individuals who love you, respect you, and have your best interest at heart, but also listen to and give an ear to those individuals who possibly don't like you and those who don't have your best interest at heart. You know, it's those individuals who may smile in your face but talk about you behind your back. It may be the one who changes the subject when you walk into a room. Oftentimes you ignore them because you just don't want to hear what they have to say. But I want to encourage you to listen and take heed to some of the whispers and hushed tones. Have you ever

walked by a room and overheard someone talking about you?
Maybe some of the following statements sound familiar:

* "He is three months behind on his mortgage because he has a gambling problem."

* "She is the only one who doesn't know that her husband is cheating on her."

* "All the makeup in the world will not hide those bruises."

* "He has been so arrogant and rude since his promotion."

* "She has gained thirty pounds in the last two weeks"

* "All the breath mints in the world won't hide the alcohol on his breath."

Although these statements are harsh, hurtful, and even cruel, can they be true of you? Is it possible that you intentionally ignore such whispers because you don't want to confront or face possible truths? Lastly, listen to that soft still voice that comes from somewhere deep within your heart, your core.

Look

Take a good look around. Take a good look at where you live. Are you still renting or sharing a room? Is it possible that you're living in your mother's basement, or possibly sleeping in a friend's guest room, or on a friend's couch? Is it possible that what started as a temporary living arrangement has now turned into something permanent? Is it possible that you're living in the exact or similar environments? It's easy to become comfortable and complacent within these living arrangements. Is this true of you? Take a good look at your place of employment. Had you planned to stay that long at that job? Have you ever thought about starting your own business? Take a look at your paycheck, and ask yourself, is it enough to get you through the month? Lastly, take a good look at your mirror. Are you still wearing that thick makeup to cover up the bruises, the black eye? Are you still wearing those dark sunglasses to hide the blood shot eyes, which will reveal that you had been up half the night drinking? Are you still wearing that mask, that big fake smile that you plaster on your face every day before you leave the house? Are you attempting to cover up or disguise the pain, depression, stress and strains of your life? I do understand that this can be extremely difficult, but nevertheless I want to encourage you to go ahead and take a good look.

Investigate

Have you ever taken the time to investigate and take an inventory of your life? Have you recently taken an Inventory of your finances? Do you know your exact net worth? Have you ever considered calculating the exact amount of your assets and liabilities? For example, if you have $1,000 in savings and $5,000 in credit card debt, then you really don't have any savings. Inventory your friendships; test to see which friends show up in a time of need. A friend shared with me that she was once desperate and in need of $200. So, she sent out a mass text to about fifteen of her closest friends in hopes of getting a quick response. Many, did not respond to the text; four called, not truly concerned or caring but they were more inquisitive and maybe nosy. They called and asked for more details of why she needed the money. Then there was only one who showed up with the money in hand, with no questions asked. Go ahead, investigate your friendships; see who will show up in time of need. Take a close look at your physical well-being. When was the last time you had a complete physical? Do you feel strong, healthy and energetic? If not, investigate why. Have you recently conducted an inventory of your spiritual growth or your mental well-being? Are you currently happy or sad? Investigate why; and if need be, ask others who can help you find the answers. When you closely examine these areas of your life, your findings may surprise you.

Nothing

After you ask, listen, look and investigate, I suggest that your next step is to do nothing. Yes, that is correct; I literally mean, do nothing. I suggest that you momentarily step away from the hustle and bustle of your busy schedule and step away from your to-do list. Life can become extremely hectic, especially for parents. They are often caring for children, their spouses, and oftentimes aging parents. Many of us are constantly on the go; it's because of the fast-paced world in which we live. Nevertheless, it's so important and even necessary to carve out time for yourself and do you. "Do you" is a term I often use when encouraging individuals to focus on themselves and their self-care. "Doing you" may be something as simple as taking a nap or staying in the shower, or soaking in the tub for an extra 10 or 15 minutes. Although taking time out for one's self-care can be difficult, it's nevertheless very much needed. I suggest that you do so as often as possible. Find ways and create opportunities to put yourself first by doing absolutely nothing. By doing so it can help you reflect, rewind, reset, and possibly equip and better prepare you for your next task and future goals. In addition to deciding to be all in, lastly, I would love for you to take away with you the three following action steps: step in, step out, and step up.

Step in

Stepping in is the ability to quiet the noise and the busyness of the outside world in order to reflect and search one's heart. One example would be the time I transitioned from high school to college. I recall finishing up my junior year of high school. During that time, I often thought about my senior year and even more about college. I had so many questions and even more decisions to make. For example, which college should I attend, and how would I pay for it? I wondered which career path I should take and where should I live? To answer many of these questions I had to first seek out trusted advisors, counselors, family members and friends. I considered their advice then I weighed my options. Before I made my final decisions, I stepped in. In other words, I searched for my true heart's desire. I deeply contemplated on things that I wanted to achieve in life. In short, the act of stepping in is taking a close look at your life, reflecting, weighing your options, and then deciding what it is that you truly want. Do you know your heart's desires? Do you know what God desires for your life? If not, then I suggest that you get off by yourself and find a quiet place where you are less likely to be disturbed or distracted. I suggest you cut your television and radio off and silence your cell phone. You must find ways to slow down this fast pace and busy world in which we live, even if it's only momentarily. We generally move forward and fast through this life without doing the things we truly aspire and like to do. We get so busy with all of life's responsibilities that very seldom do we take time to focus on ourselves. To rectify that situation, I suggest that you take time to meditate, pray, and seek God's face. Somehow and in some way, make great attempts to focus on your hearts' desires. Once you step in and discover whatever it is that you desire, whatever it may be that you would like to accomplish, then immediately step out.

Step Out

Stepping out is the act of formulating and implementing a plan. Once you have decided on some things you truly love to do and want to accomplish, immediately devise a plan to move in that direction. In order for you to reach your goals, most likely, you will have to step out of your comfort zones. Most likely, you will be expected to do some things you've never done before, which often brings up doubt, feelings of intimidation, and fear. Nevertheless, it's imperative that you immediately make plans and move toward your goals. When we don't quickly act on our plans, we often become stagnated and begin to procrastinate. Oftentimes doubt develops and then you find yourself putting things off and resting in your comfort zone of procrastination. As the years go by, you might find yourself with a plan but unfortunately, without any movement or action, this can leave you stuck and immovable without any results. Now if you want something different, you're going to have to do something different, and stepping out of your comfort zone starts the process. You cannot get to where you want to be by staying where you are. So, if you must step out nervously, trembling, and possibly crying with knocking knees, then do so. It will be so worth it. No matter how challenging, uncomfortable or fearful it might be, please make the decision to step out. That choice, that one act of bravery, that act of stepping out of your comfort zone has the ability to transform your life.

Step Up

Once you have reflected and focused on what it is that you truly desire, made plans and made a great effort to go after it, followed by successfully achieving it, then repeat the entire process but on another level. Stepping up is the mental and or physical ability to continuously improve and increase. It's basically making a decision not to become stagnated, or settling on one's current platform. It's the ability to make a conscious decision to simply elevate your life to the next level of increase. The act of leveling up helps prevent you from becoming stuck or possibly falling into comfort zones of mediocrity or becoming mundane. Whatever level or platform you may presently be on, decide to step up and take life a notch higher. It can be a baby step or a leap, but whichever step you may take, please let it be a step up. Do not remain on the same level for the rest of your life. Let me share with you some brief examples of leveling up. Maybe you worked very hard to obtain your bachelor's degree; ok you might now want to consider going back to school for your master's degree. You may have worked extremely hard to lose the extra pounds and improve your health. So, you might now want to consider running a marathon or signing up for other physical competitions. Have you raised your children? Are they grown and have families of their own? Maybe you can now start that business, write the book or do whatever it is that you have been promising yourself to do.

I must inform you that stepping up does not always initially appear to be elevation or increase. Sometimes stepping up actually may require you to step down or do less. It may seem as if I'm now contradicting myself, but I'm not; let me share an example with you. An employee working in an executive position is overworked and overwhelmed, which has drastically increased their stress levels. The highly stressed employee decides to take a demotion, with less responsibility and less pay. This single act of bravery and or possibly an act of desperation immediately decreased their stress, and over time their health improved. Over time he sought employment elsewhere. He was able to secure another executive position and increased pay with less stress. Initially, he appeared to be stepping down but it was a means to stepping up. So, if you must step down, or step to the side let it be a means to stepping up.

Reflection

My hope is that the book has shed some light on some possible broken areas within your life. Within the first chapter, I shared with you some personal broken areas that I discovered in my own life. I also explained and gave a detailed example of what it actually means to be broken and not to be aware of it. Within the meat of the book, I became even more transparent. I shared many of my broken life experiences. My aspiration is that the examples would provide insight and create a desire to immediately review, and investigate the different areas of your life. Within the ending of the book, I offered solutions, exactly twelve steps which I implemented within my own personal life which have drastically changed my life. My final hope is that you take an objective look at your life, contemplate and then decide if this is how you want to live out the remainder of your life. If the answer is yes, congratulations; you rank amongst a few and only a handful of individuals. If the answer is no then I